Waterstone's
Guide to Children's Books

Edited by Alyx Price
General Editors Michelle Birch *(1st Edition)*
and Tessa MacGregor *(2nd Edition)*

Contents

INTRODUCTION

"All she thought about the key was that if it was the key to the closed garden, and she could find where the door was, she could perhaps open it and see what was inside the walls . . .

if she liked it she could go into it every day . . . she could make up some play of her own . . ."

The Secret Garden by Frances Hodgson Burnett

Nothing can replace that special feeling of being lost in a book; entering that magical world where anything can happen. The amazing worlds of CS Lewis and Roald Dahl, the crazy rhymes of Dr Seuss and the fun discovery of The Hungry Caterpillar stay with their readers forever.

Waterstone's knows that regardless of all the other distractions children have, they still want to read. Bookwatch, the compilers of bestseller lists, confirms that the sales of children's books rise consistently year on year. This matches our experience at Waterstone's.

The astounding choice of books for children and the number of new titles published each month creates a new problem. Where to start? How do you find the right book for a child? This guide offers what we feel to be the best of classic and contemporary books for all ages and it is age ranged to make it easier to find the books in our stores.

We particularly hope that this guide will give you and your child an exciting introduction to the world of children's stories and that it will help to foster a lifetime love of books.

Let Waterstone's be the key to your discovery . . .

How to use this guide

Each book review is presented in the following format:

TITLE
Author/illustrator
Publisher, cover (hardback or paperback) price and ISBN - to order the book
Review written by booksellers

The symbol **"** represents audio books and ☆ prize winners.
The Guide is divided into 7 main sections, roughly chronological by age.
The subject index will help you with special needs and interests.
There is also an author and title index.
All books in the Guide can be obtained through Waterstone's, subject
to availability.
The reading age is not always given. Sometimes it is self explanatory
(all titles in 'Young Adults' are for 12-15 year olds), and sometimes
the age range is unrestricted.

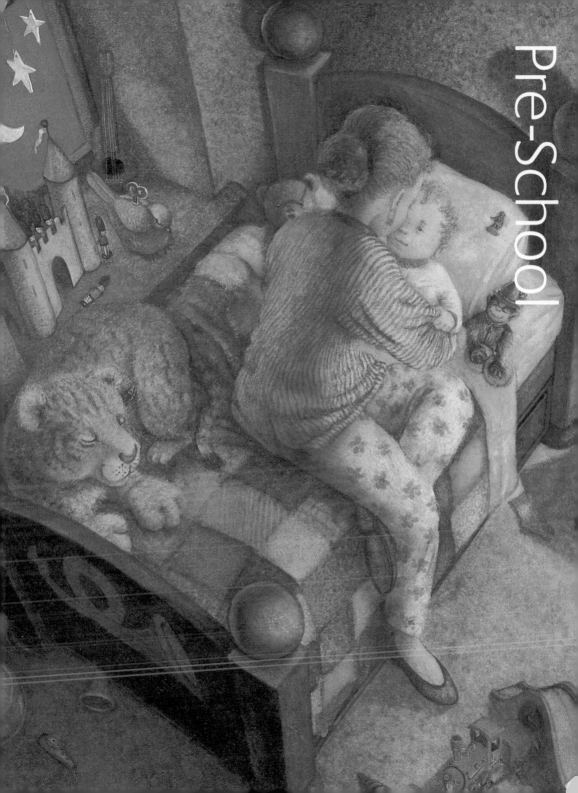

PRE-SCHOOL

A love of books can be nurtured from a very early age. Stories and pictures take children on a magical journey of imagination and discovery.

Babies love cloth books; they are tactile, soft and safe for them to have as their own. Toddlers have a huge variety of board books available to them, as many of the classic picture books have been adapted for the enjoyment of a younger age group.

We have chosen a range of pre-school books including stories, nursery rhymes and pop-ups. There are first experience and early learning books, which introduce everything from ABC and colours to potty training and staying the night away from home – all the new things that children need reassurance to understand.

There is a style of picture book to suit every child – and they will soon latch on to their favourites. We have chosen both the familiar award-winning classics as well as newer titles which you will be able to discover and enjoy with your child. Sharing stories is a vital part of enjoying books at this age. It opens up discussions of situations and soothes and introduces these amazing, imaginary worlds which stay with you forever.

The books in this pre-school section have wonderful stories and big surprises. They will stimulate discussion and laughter and help to develop a relationship with books.

WE'RE GOING ON A BEAR HUNT

BABY BOOKS

BUGGY BUDDIES
Emily Bolam
Campbell Books hb £2.99
These great little books come with a plastic spiral strap to attach them to highchairs, buggies or cots. They are bright, have simple stories about various animals and, best of all, stay where you put them!

WEBSTER'S WARDROBE
Claire and Maarten Bos
Bloomsbury £5.99 074753795X
Vibrant colours and nonsense sing-song verse make this board book fun to look at and to shout out loud. Webster Seal puts on lots of animal suits to brighten up his own grey colour.

MY FARM
Rod Campbell
Macmillan £5.99 0333659988
An interactive cloth book with lift-the-flap pages. There are chicks to find, rabbit tails to touch and piglets that actually squeak on this farm!

THE VERY HUNGRY CATERPILLAR
Eric Carle
Hamish Hamilton hb £4.99
0241003008
Carle's definitive style combines perfectly well with this sturdy board book. The holes through the fruit are ideal for little fingers and no one could ever tire of the story. Some of his other titles are also available in board books.

LUCY COUSINS' CLOTH BOOKS
Lucy Cousins
Walker £3.99
In these four books Lucy Cousins uses the park, home, farm and garden as scenes for her bold and colourful pictures.

TOUCH AND FEEL
Dorling Kindersley £4.99
Books for little people become really exciting with these titles. Not only are there big colourful photographs but children can also touch the pictures and discover for themselves the difference between the texture of a soft chick and a woolly sheep at the farm or a kitten and a towel at home.

Excellent Extras
Mick Inkpen's name is real, but it has nothing to do with writing. Ink means bog and pen means hill. Mick Boghill? Maybe he should stick with Inkpen.

WIBBLY PIG BOARD BOOKS
Mick Inkpen
Hodder Children's Books £2.99
Wibbly Pig charms everyone who reads these books. No home should be without him. Follow him in his adventures as he eats bananas, makes pictures, opens presents and much more.

CAT IS SLEEPY
Satoshi Kitamura
Andersen hb £2.99
0862646693
Lively distinctive pictures and a simple story make this board book a huge favourite with parents and children.

FIRST FOCUS BABY BOOKS
Ladybird £2.99 - £3.99
These range from cloth books to bath books and board books. Ladybird use strong, contrasting colours, or black and white images for the very young, and their bold images make these ideal first books for babies. They are age-ranged on the cover to indicate suitability.

ELMER BOARD BOOKS
David McKee
Andersen £3.99
Elmer is a patchwork elephant who shows very young children that it's alright to be different from everyone else.
Also available as picture books.

WINNIE THE POOH PADDED BOARD BOOKS

Methuen £3.99

Just right for little hands, these books have simple stories and pictures about all the favourite characters. They are also usefully made of durable laminated board in case of accidents!

PEACE AT LAST

Jill Murphy
Campbell Books hb £3.99
0333712773

Mr Bear cannot sleep. He just seems to be surrounded by too much noise whatever he tries. This is an old favourite which works really well as a board book.

THE RAINBOW FISH

Marcus Pfister
Ragged Bears hb £6.99
1558585362

Rainbow Fish thinks he is too beautiful to play with the other fish and soon becomes very lonely. The key to his happiness is to share his lovely scales with others. The special thing about this book is that the scales really are shiny.

DR. SEUSS BOARD BOOKS

Dr. Seuss
Collins hb £4.50

A selection of the most straightforward beginner books have been turned into board books for younger children. They are bright and sturdy with all the expected silliness. A great introduction to the crazy world of Dr. Seuss.

DINOSAUR ROAR!

Paul and Henrietta Stickland
Ragged Bears hb £4.99
1857141296

The colourful dinosaurs race through this book. This is a fun rhyming board book of opposites.

EARLY LEARNING

THE FIRST THOUSAND WORDS

Heather Amery & Stephen Cartwright
Usborne pb £5.99 0746023022

Usborne's new, revised edition of 'First Thousand Words' provides the young reader with a fun and clear way to learn new words. A straightforward but also stimulating way to learn the language.

LITTLE RABBIT'S FIRST NUMBER BOOK

Alan Baker
Kingfisher hb £8.99
0753402882

From simple number recognition and counting to finding the right number of matching animals. This is an attractive book which combines fun with learning numbers.

ONE TWO THREE WITH ANT AND BEE

Angela Banner
Heinemann hb £4.99
0434929646

This is just one in the little series about these funny characters. Ant is sick and the counting story includes all the things that he will need to keep him occupied in bed. The numbers are highlighted in red for emphasis.

Excellent Extras

In letterland, Sammy Snake makes lots of noise so Harry Hatman has to stand next to him to make him "Sh"!

LETTERLAND ABC

Collins hb £10.99 0003034186

Letterland is a very special place where children can see letters brought vividly to life through colourful characters. Extremely stimulating text and illustrations make this an invaluable introduction to the alphabet.

Lucy Cousins

Lucy Cousins is best loved for her many Maisy books. Find out below how and why she created her.

Author by author

When I was little I used to read the Lucy and Tom books by Shirley Hughes. My brother is called Tom, and the illustrations always looked very much like our house, so I used to like thinking they were sort of about us. I like reading them now to my children, because I remember the illustrations very vividly. I don't know what my inspiration for creating Maisy was. At College I came up with the idea of a pull tab book about taking clothes on and off. I wanted an animal character, and sat down and drew some different animals. Maisy appeared on the page.

I never stop thinking about getting new ideas. I just sit down to work with a blank sheet of paper and whatever ideas come into my head at that moment go down on paper. If anything inspires me it's my own children. They range in age from 2-8, so for several years I've lived with children of the age for whom I'm creating books, which helps enormously. "Happy Birthday Maisy" started being created the week following my son Olly's 4th birthday. The cards that Maisy gets for her birthday are from my four children – Josie, Olly, Rufus and Ben.

Some books by Lucy Cousins:

Maisy's ABC
Maisy's Happy Birthday
Maisy Goes To The Farm
Maisy Goes To Bed
Maisy Goes Swimming
published by walker

IT'S A SHOELACE!
Sue Hendra
Bloomsbury hb £7.99
0747523320
Great fun for young children. Yellow monster and his friends wonder what the string is that runs through the book. Is it a tightrope or spaghetti? Of course it's a shoelace and the book ends with a step by step guide to how to tie them.

LUCY AND TOM'S ABC
Shirley Hughes
Puffin pb £3.99 0140505210
Shirley Hughes' delightful third book in this series takes children of any age through the alphabet. Each letter is depicted by everyday, familiar situations. Every page is rich with traditional illustrations which reveal the warmth and happiness of childhood.

ONE SMILING GRANDMA
Anne Marie Linden
Mammoth pb £4.99
0749725001
This is a Caribbean counting book. A little girl thinks of all the different things that remind her of being with her grandma. The numbers count through a variety of vibrant scenes.

FLORA MCDONNELL'S ABC
Flora McDonnell
Walker pb £5.99 0744560071
Both capital and small letters are illustrated in this book. BEAR contrasts with butterfly and ELEPHANT with egg. Words and bright, colourful pictures combined make this a memorable alphabet book.

I CAN SPELL WITH 3 LETTERS
Anna Nilson
Kingfisher hb £6.99
075340172X
This is an inspired way of making spelling fun. 75 pictures illustrate 3 letter words which can be spelled out on the flip cards. The book works at its best if adult and child spend time doing this together. There is also a version with 4 letters.

BABY AND TODDLER'S BIG BOOK OF EVERYTHING
Roger Priddy
Dorling Kindersley hb £8.99
075135466X
Various subjects are illustrated with big bright photographs. This is an exciting treasury of words.

BABAR AND HIS BIG BOOK OF WORDS
Ragged Bears hb £12.99
1857141342
Various scenes from the world of Babar are used to introduce new words. The familiar characters help to make it seem more like a story and less like a picture dictionary. The little mouse hiding on each page adds to the comforting feel of this book.

MOUSE PAINT
Ellen Stoll Walsh
Orchard pb £3.99 1852135719
The mice fall into different pots of paint and as they make puddles on the floor they find out which other colours can be made from yellow, blue and red. This is a gentle story which is good for developing interest in colour.

DO PIGS HAVE STRIPES?
Melanie Walsh
Mammoth pb £4.99
0749730269
Does a bird have a big black wet nose? With simple questions and clever illustrations that give a child clues to the answers, this is a good picture book for introducing more unusual animals.

MY FIRST WORD BOOK
Angela Wilkes
Dorling Kindersley £7.99
0863186300
A first picture dictionary containing over 1,000 words commonly used by young children. The clear photographs illustrating each word encourage easy recognition whilst the thematic design stimulates discussion. This book will help with simple vocabulary building as well as counting and early reading. It also comes as a big hardback.

FIRST EXPERIENCES

Catherine and Laurence Anholt

Catherine and Laurence Anholt write books which invite children into a world of new experiences. Their books are warm and colourful and because they are often told from a child's point of view they are ultimately reassuring.

BILLY AND THE BIG NEW SCHOOL
Catherine and Laurence Anholt
Orchard pb £4.99 1860395244
Billy feels 'a little funny inside' about starting school. Using a parallel story of a tiny sparrow who flies the nest, the Anholts sum up all the emotions that children feel before they make this big step and also introduce all the good things that happen during a school day.

WHAT MAKES ME HAPPY?
Catherine and Laurence Anholt
Walker pb £4.99
0744543746
With gentle illustrations this book asks simple questions about emotions and offers a variety of answers for discussion. The strength of this book is that it is told through children's own eyes and allows them to consider their feelings themselves

ELLA AND THE NAUGHTY LION
Russell Ayto and Anne Cottinger
Mammoth pb £4.99
0749730196
When Ella's baby brother first comes home a naughty lion slips in through the door and begins to do very bad things. The more cross Ella feels the worse he behaves. A subtle book about the issues of sibling rivalry.

THE POP-UP POTTY BOOK
Marianne Borgardt
Orion hb £5.99 1858811406
All the mystery of the potty is taken away in this fun lift-the-flap and pull-the-tab story.

I LIKE IT WHEN...

ARTHUR'S CHICKEN POX
Marc Brown
Red Fox pb £2.50 0099263149
Arthur is an aardvark who
has a cheeky sister called
D.W. Together they have lots
of adventures and so create
a fun series which talks about
all kinds of new experiences
like having pets, birthday
parties and baby-sitting. In
this story Arthur may not
be able to go to the circus
because he is ill and D.W
gives his ticket away to her
friend! But maybe everything
will be all right by Saturday...

USBORNE FIRST EXPERIENCES
Anne Civardi & Stephen Cartwright
Usborne pb £2.99
An excellent series of simple
stories which introduce
young children to new
situations which they find
difficult to understand.
Amongst the 'First
Experiences' covered are
flying, visiting the dentist
and moving house.

ZA-ZA'S BABY BROTHER
Lucy Cousins
Walker pb £4.99 0744547644
The zebra family are having a
new baby. The story talks
about all the changes which
can upset an older sibling.
It encourages the older child
to make friends with the baby
and reminds them that there
is still time for them.

GOING TO PLAYSCHOOL
Sarah Garland
Puffin pb £3.99 0140553630
Sarah Garland takes the
fear out of that first day at
playschool with bright and
comforting illustrations and
simple text.

BABY DUCK AND THE NEW EYEGLASSES
Amy Hest
Walker pb £4.99
0744552206
Baby Duck hates her new
glasses. She looks funny
and what will she do if they
fall off? Luckily Grandpa
saves the day. This is an
encouraging read for any
child who feels defeated.

EAT YOUR DINNER!
Virginia Miller
Walker Books pb £3.99
0744531411
Virginia Miller's most
popular books are about
small bear Ba and his father
George. Playful and
independent Bartholomew
says "Nah" to everything –
that is until he says "Aah"
and earns himself a great
big bear hug. You can read
about them in 'Get into Bed!'
and 'On your Potty' too.

I LIKE IT WHEN . . .
Mary Murphy
Mammoth pb £4.99
0749731192
These lovable characters
illustrate a really special
relationship. Throughout
the day the little penguin
talks about ordinary things
which are best because they
are done together with the
big penguin. This is a warm
story to share and repeat.

I WANT MY POTTY
Tony Ross
Collins pb £4.50 0006626874
Tony Ross encapsulates the
madcap adventures of any
family toilet-training its child.
This is a perfect introduction
to the functions of potties for
any child under 5 years old.

MY MANY COLOURED DAYS
Dr. Seuss
Hutchinson hb £9.99
009176890X
Moods, both good and bad,
are hard to understand.
This rhyming picture book
associates them with colours
and makes everything clearer
for adults and children.

Allan Ahlberg

Allan Ahlberg has published over 100 books for children. From picture books like Monkey Do to Happy Families to novels like The Giant Baby and Woof. His stories often come from the magical land of his own childhood.

He was adopted into a poor family where there was not money for books. In fact until he was ten he only owned 6 books and these were given to him as Sunday School prizes each year. His favourite picture book when he was small was called 'The Bear That Nobody Wanted' which he read and re-read a hundred times. He liked the title so much that he used it for one of his own books.

At school he was so excited when he wrote his stories that his handwriting and spelling were terrible. He even forgot to put in some of the words because he couldn't write fast enough! Miss Scriven, his English teacher, said she did enjoy the bits she could understand. By the time he was 14 he knew he wanted to be a writer – if he couldn't be a footballer!

His favourite book of his own? Bye Bye Baby with its gentle rhythm and pictures but he says he changes his mind every day.

Some books by Alan Alhberg
Peepo
Each Peach Pear Plum
Monkey Do
Burglar Bill
Dinosaur Dreams
The Giant Baby
The Jolly Postman
Published by Walker, Puffin & Mammoth

EDWARD'S FIRST NIGHT AWAY

Rosemary Wells
Walker pb £4.50
0744552591

A night away from home can often be a large hurdle. Edward Bear has to stay the night at his friend's house because of the snow. The story gives reassuring preparation tips so that children know what to expect.

NURSERY RHYMES

THE OXFORD NURSERY BOOK

Ian Beck
Oxford UP pb £5.99
0192723227

Ian Beck's beautiful and distinctive illustrations make this an enchanting collection of nursery rhymes, poems and lullabies.

FIRST VERSES: ACTION RHYMES

John Foster and Carol Thompson
Oxford pb and tape £6.99
019276179X

Children can turn themselves into robots, rockets and elephants using the tape to sing to and looking at the picture book to find the movements. There are also counting, finger and chanting rhymes in this fun and imaginative series.

A FIRST PICTURE BOOK OF NURSERY RHYMES

Elizabeth Harbour
Puffin pb £4.99
ISBN 0140549730

Beautiful, detailed pictures create a whole new world for these nursery rhymes and make this book completely absorbing.

A CHILD'S TREASURY OF NURSERY RHYMES

Katy MacDonald Denton
Kingfisher hb £14.99
0753401436

A lovely collection of rhymes that children can grow with. Beginning with lullabies and ending with playground action rhymes, this book has both familiar and unusual verses.

THIS LITTLE PUFFIN

Elizabeth Matterson
Puffin pb £5.99 0140340483

A comprehensive source book of rhymes and songs for young children. Music is often included, as well as suggestions on how to play the games.

MY VERY FIRST MOTHER GOOSE

Iona Opie, illustrated by Rosemary Wells
Walker hb £14.99
0744544009

A collection of traditional rhymes with Rosemary Wells' sweetest animal illustrations. Bright and colourful this is an ideal present for a young child.

POP-UPS AND NOVELTY BOOKS

THE JOLLY POSTMAN (OR OTHER PEOPLE'S LETTERS)

Janet & Allan Ahlberg
Methuen hb £8.99
0434925152

A children's classic. Follow the Jolly Postman on his rounds and actually pull out and read the letters he delivers!

Also available:
THE JOLLY POCKET POSTMAN
THE JOLLY CHRISTMAS POSTMAN

KATY CAT AND BEAKY BOO
Lucy Cousins
Walker hb £12.99
0744544661

Find out about these two friends by lifting the flaps and learning about numbers, clothes and other everyday things. Bright and happy pictures make this a book that all children love.

MAISY GOES TO PLAYSCHOOL
Lucy Cousins
Walker Books hb £6.99
074525063

These books form part of a series of delightful interactive stories about Maisy the mouse. Children pull tabs and lift flaps as they help Maisy get ready for bed or have fun at playschool. The pictures are bold and bright and the flaps are sturdy enough to withstand the onslaught of little hands.

ALL KINDS OF PEOPLE
Emma Damon
Tango hb £7.99 1857070674

Everyone is different and here you can lift the flaps to see how. Whether tall, big, with freckles or with short hair it doesn't matter because everyone is special.

SALLY'S AMAZING COLOUR BOOK
Paul Dowling
Andersen hb £8.99
0862648017

Sally spends a week with her Granny. As she busies herself there are lots of tabs to pull and lots of surprises in this colourful interactive book.

THE WIDE-MOUTHED FROG
Keith Faulkner
Madcap hb £5.99
023399100X

The wide-mouthed frog wants to know what other animals eat. Until he meets an animal who gives him a big surprise. This is a fantastic pop-up story.

MOLE'S SUMMER STORY
Richard Fowler
Transworld hb £5.99
0385407297

Adopt the role of mole as you guide him through his summer holiday. An ingeniously simple idea which aids dexterity and encourages inventive story telling.

EVERYONE HIDE FROM WIBBLY PIG
Mick Inkpen
Hodder pb £6.99 0340681381

Wibbly Pig is playing hide and seek. Help him to find his friends by lifting the flaps. Tiny Pig has found a great hiding place. Will you be able to find him?

THE VERY VISIBLE MOUSE
Anne Merrick and Tessa Richardson-Jones
Bloomsbury pb £5.99
0747530637

These mice have been brought up to to keep a very low profile in Mr and Mrs Jones' house. But Calamity Mouse decides to do her own thing. Lift the flaps to find all the nooks and crannies where the mice hide.

SAM'S SANDWICH
David Pelham
Cape hb £5.99 0224030116

Naughty Sam makes his sister a sandwich full of nasty surprises. Good fun! Sam has more revolting adventures in 'Sam's Surprise' and 'The Sensational Samburger'.

SAY CHEESE
David Pelham
Cape hb £8.99 0224046438

Enter into an exciting mouse world where Grandma Mouse wants to hold a big family party. The pop-ups are ingenious and the story all takes place in a book which looks like an inviting piece of cheese!

PEEPO!

EACH PEACH PEAR PLUM

PICTURE BOOKS

The great thing about picture books is that they can be enjoyed by a whole range of children. They can be shared by the young and old or read independently by school children (see 'Young Readers'). Because of this we have not given the following titles age-bands.

A CHEESE AND TOMATO SPIDER
Nick Sharratt
Scholastic hb £8.99
0590542613
Mix and match the words and pictures to create strange and wonderful crazy things. See an exploding granny and a police cake. Create your own mixed-up world.

FUZZY YELLOW DUCKLINGS
Matthew Van Fleet
Ragged Bears hb £8.99
1857140842
This simple idea introduces texture, colour, shape and animals; a woolly white rectangle becomes a sheep when the page is opened out. At the back is a fold-out picture to point things out and confirm what has been learnt along the way.

BIG YELLOW TAXI
Ken Wilson-Max
Ragged Bears hb £7.99
1856022250
Take the taxi for a drive in this interactive book. Pull the tabs to fill it with petrol, put seatbelts on and travel through the countryside. You can collect a receipt and finish off at the carwash.

WHEELS ON THE BUS
Paul Zelinsky
Orchard hb £8.50 1852132728
A favourite song, graphically depicted in a book filled with moving parts.

EACH PEACH PEAR PLUM
Janet & Allan Ahlberg
Puffin pb £4.99 0140509194
This book takes pre-school children on a delightful journey through popular nursery rhymes whilst playing 'I Spy'.

PEEPO!
Janet & Allan Ahlberg
Puffin pb £4.99 0140503846
Highly recommended book in verse, showing baby's day from morning until night with the aid of a cut-out peephole.

Helen Cooper

Helen Cooper was born in London, and brought up in Cumbria. She published her first book in 1987 and has gone on to publish several favourites since. Her books for younger children capture the imagination very well and this is why.

Author by author

Childhood experiences fuel my stories. Once a bear came to my house to live under the stairs. Even when I wrote and illustrated 'The Bear Under The Stairs' I still couldn't decide whether the bear was really there or not; I've left that decision to my readers.

When a child and a grown-up read my books together, I want them both to have fun. I like to write short rhythmical texts which are easy to read, leaving lots of time for exploring the illustrations. These are filled with lots of detail so there's something new to find with each reading (and I hope there are many).

Ideas for my illustrations come from any which way. While on holiday with my husband we spent a few autumn afternoons amidst colossal piles of pumpkins for sale on the New England roadsides. You can find out just where these pumpkins ended up - my new book is called 'Pumpkin Soup'.

Some books by Helen Cooper

Pumpkin Soup
The Baby Who Wouldn't Go To Bed
(Kate Greenaway medal winner 1997)
The Bear Under The Stairs
all published by Doubleday and Picture Corgi

WHERE'S MY TEDDY?
Jez Alborough
Walker pb £3.99 074453058X
Rhythmic, rhyming story about the sudden panic of losing your teddy bear. Wonderful for sharing with three year olds, as well as for older children to read themselves.

HEAVEN
Nicholas Allan
Red Fox pb £3.99
0099653419
Lily finds out that Dill the Dog needs to go up to heaven because he has been called by the angels. So begins a gentle, funny discussion of different perceptions of heaven.

THE LIGHTHOUSE KEEPER'S LUNCH
Rhonda & David Armitage
Scholastic pb £3.99 0590551752
A humorous story with lots of ingredients to amuse and entertain. The seagulls who steal the lighthouse keeper's lunch have cartoon-type speech bubbles which children can read aloud.

THOMAS THE TANK ENGINE
Reverend Awdry
Heinemann hb £4.99
0434803782
Reverend Awdry started this series 50 years ago and his son Christopher has proudly carried on the tradition, delighting yet another generation. (New format)

THE MOUSEHOLE CAT
Antonia Barber, illustrations Nicola Bayley
Walker Books pb £4.99
0744523532
Enchanting Cornish folk tale of Mowzer the cat and his master, Tom the fisherman, who save the village of Mousehole from the Great Storm Cat. Bewitching full page illustrations.

PETER AND THE WOLF
Ian Beck
Corgi pb £3.95 0552527556
A wonderful re-telling of Prokofiev's classic tale with jewel-bright pictures. Superb for family story-time, especially if it is read along with the music from the tape.

Quentin Blake

Perhaps best known for his hilarious illustrations for many of Roald Dahl's books, Quentin Blake has also been writing and illus-trating his own books for 30 years.

CLOWN
Quentin Blake
Red Fox pb £4.99 0099493616
The illustrations tell the story in this unusual picture book about the clown who is thrown away and needs to find a new home. The lack of text gives children the opportunity to invent and then re-invent the story around the frame-work. A book you will never become tired of.

SIMPKIN
Quentin Blake
Red Fox pb £4.50 0099302306
Blake's hilarious illustrations bring to life this child's introduction to the world of opposites. Simple rhymes take us through Simpkin's day and his extremes of behaviour. A fun story to read aloud.

Raymond Briggs

Raymond Briggs is an accomplished author/ illustrator who has the enviable talent of being able to write for children of all ages. His books are often good for encourag-ing more reluctant readers.

THE BEAR
Raymond Briggs
Red Fox pb £4.99 0099385619
A very large polar bear comes to visit Tilly. It seems he's here to stay and she has a very busy day looking after him; he comes with bear-size problems. There is a lovely mixture of text and dreamy pictures which go so well with the sense of both imagination and reality.

THE SNOWMAN
Raymond Briggs
Puffin pb £4.99 0140503501
A timeless classic appealing to all ages. Wonderful illustrations and a warm-hearted story without any text. It is a perfect book for sharing at home.

WILLY THE WIMP
Anthony Browne
Walker pb £4.99 0744543630
The character Willy the gorilla will be a winner with children who have experienced bullying at school. Willy decides to make some changes so that he can get the better of his bullies, and he is soon no longer a wimp who is frightened of everything and everybody – or is he?

HANDA'S SURPRISE
Eileen Browne
Walker pb £4.99
0744536340
Handa takes a basket of fruit to her friend Akeyo. On her walk she passes a variety of interested animals. When she reaches the next village there is a surprise for everyone!

A DARK DARK TALE
Ruth Brown
Red Fox pb £4.50 0099874008
A jet-black cat steals her way deeper and deeper into a gloomy house and finally uncovers a mouse. A charming story with a recurring 'dark' motif, ideal for reading aloud.

MIFFY
Dick Bruna
World International hb £2.99
0749829796
Bruna's wonderful bold drawings and bright colours make Miffy the Rabbit easily identifiable to toddlers. Collect the series.

GRANPA
John Burningham
Puffin pb £3.99 0140508414
Granpa is the profoundly moving story of a little girl's stay with, and subsequent loss of her grandparent. Burningham conveys a sense of affectionate memory and sorrow without ever becoming morbid or over-sentimental.

OI! GET OFF OUR TRAIN
John Burningham
Red Fox pb £4.99 009985340X
A sleeping boy dreams of driving a train, aided by his loyal pyjama-case dog. On their travels the duo rescue and befriend many endangered animals. A touching tale with an environmental theme.

Nick Butterworth

Nick Butterworth began as a graphic designer before moving into children's books. His illustrations are renowned for their crisp, clear quality and their close links to the well-written text. Best known for his popular Percy the Park-Keeper books, he has also written and illustrated books for toddlers.

THE SNOWMAN

Mary Murphy

Mary Murphy produces very bold and simple picture books for the under fives. She lives in Dublin with her two dogs, Sally and Jem, and got her ideas for her work from the following:

Author by author

When I was small I wanted to be a vet or an artist. We always had lots of pets in our house and loved any books with animals in them.

When I started to work on my own books, it felt natural to have animals as the main characters. The books always start with me working on a character, doing lots of drawings of a little penguin or a little dog. Then by the time I come to work out a story idea I feel I know the character very well. I keep a file of drawings on animals ,and notebooks for ideas, in case I forget things.

The penguins and other characters aren't really based on people I know – they are really just themselves. But certainly the things they like doing are things I like too. And I get ideas sometimes from my nieces and nephews, and from older people too, and my own dogs, so I suppose there are bits of lots of people I know in my books.

Books published so far:

I like it when...
Please be Quiet!
You Smell
My Puffer Train
(Spring'99)
all published by Mammoth
and Heinemann

ONE SNOWY NIGHT
Nick Butterworth
Collins pb £4.50 0006643183

One winter's night, Percy rescues his animal friends from the cold in the first book of the series. Butterworth's illustrations are exquisitely detailed and full of gentle humour.

THUD
Nick Butterworth
Collins pb £5.99
0006646468

First an ugly beast arrives in the night and then a monster can be heard thudding through the forest. Maybe the ugly beast will help the animals to get rid of the monster. The rounded characters of the animals make this a great story.

Rod Campbell

Rod Campbell had his first book published in 1980. His books all have a learning bias with flaps and tabs and are great fun for the under fives to investigate.

DEAR ZOO
Rod Campbell
Puffin pb £4.99 014050446X

A simple story about the search for a pet. Lift the flaps to uncover each exotic but unsuitable animal the zoo sends. A wonderful book for introducing animal words to small children.

NOISY FARM
Rod Campbell
Puffin pb £4.99
0140502939

Learn farm animal names and sounds with this simple story. If you lift the flaps you can see the baby animals as well.

THE VERY HUNGRY CATERPILLAR
Eric Carle
Puffin pb £4.50 0140500871

This is the story of a small hungry caterpillar who eats his way through a variety of different foods before turning into a beautiful butterfly. A charming picture book which is also an excellent way to introduce children to counting. Also available as a board book.

DINOSAURS AND ALL THAT RUBBISH!

SOMETHING ELSE
Kathryn Cave, illustrations Chris Riddell
Puffin pb £4.99 0140549072

Something Else isn't like the others; somehow he is different even though he tries to be the same. Then Something arrives at his house and wants to be friends with him. Something Else is not sure but maybe they could accept each other?

I LOVE YOU, BLUE KANGAROO

Emma Chichester-Clark
Andersen hb £9.99
0862648319

Lily loves Blue Kangaroo but she is distracted by all the other toys that she is given. Blue Kangaroo is very upset and hurt and Lily almost loses him to her baby brother forever. Beautiful pictures with lots of feeling.

PRINCESS SMARTYPANTS

Babette Cole
Puffin pb £4.50 0140555269

Great illustrations, great story. A twist on the old princess-must-marry-a-prince theme. This princess knows what's what and stays happily unmarried in the company of her pets. A memorable anti-stereotype, funny story.

SO MUCH

Trish Cooke
Walker pb £5.99
0744543967

One by one all the family come round to visit Mum and Baby. Each of them fusses over Baby in their own way and baby wants to play forever. But it's soon bedtime and Baby can sleep knowing he is loved and cared for. The illustrations and characters just jump from the page in this warm book.

THE BABY WHO WOULDN'T GO TO BED

Helen Cooper
Corgi pb £4.99 0552528382

The Baby wants to stay up all night and so, with lots of energy, sets off on an adventure in his little car. But all his friends want to sleep; the soldiers, the train and even the moon. Alone in a sleepy land there is only one other person still awake. This captures the fantasy of a child's twilight world.

THE BEAR UNDER THE STAIRS

Helen Cooper
Corgi pb £3.99 0552527068

More than just a useful tale in helping children overcome fears of dark spaces this book has rich, magical illustrations and a wonderful sense of humour.

THREADBEAR

NOAH'S ARK

Retold and illustrated by
Lucy Cousins
Walker pb £4.99 0744536723

A vibrant and cheerful approach to a popular Old Testament story. A clear and simple text and illustration leave lots of scope for children to add their own narrative (and animal noises!).
Also available in board book.

HAIRY MACLARY FROM DONALDSON'S DAIRY

Lynley Dodd
Puffin pb £3.99 0140505318

The first in a series featuring the scruffy dog and his friends all of whom have equally catchy names. Children love the rhyme, repetition and rhythm of these best-selling stories.

HAPPY DAYS FOR MOUSE AND MOLE

Joyce Dunbar, illustrated by
James Mayhew
Corgi pb £3.99 0552529788

Gentle, dreamy stories with these two friends. Together they laze in the garden, search for Mole's spectacles and catch falling autumn leaves. Perfect to read aloud.

DINOSAURS AND ALL THAT RUBBISH

Michael Foreman
Puffin pb £4.99 014055260X

First published in 1972, this book raises issues which are now familiar, yet were unusual for a children's book at the time of publication. When Man decides to explore a distant star, he leaves the Earth in a terrible mess. He can only return to Earth if he learns to care for it. A book for any child who takes an interest in the world around them.

OLIVER'S VEGETABLES

Vivian French & Alison Bartlett
Hodder pb £4.99 0340634790

An original and strikingly visual story about a boy who will only eat chips. One day he goes to stay with his grandparents, and discovers that maybe he can like vegetables after all.

MR BEAR TO THE RESCUE

Debi Gliori
Orchard pb £4.99 1860394744

There is a terrible storm in the forest and the small animals need Mr Bear's help. He leaves the warmth of his bed and bravely goes to see what he can do.

ROW YOUR BOAT

Pippa Goodhart, illustrations
Stephen Lambert
Mammoth pb £4.99
0749731591

This traditional song gains more verses and becomes a truly magical journey in a rowing boat. You can act out the story and become each of the animals or you can sit and relax with the beautiful pictures which themselves take you into another world.

THE MEGAMOGS

Peter Haswell
Red Fox pb £4.50 009926661X

Miss Marbletop's cats are called the Megamogs. When she goes away Kevin Catflap takes charge and he has BIG plans to keep the other cats occupied. Expressive pictures and great wordplay make this a very funny book.

KATIE MORAG AND THE WEDDING

Mairi Hedderwick
Collins pb £4.50
0099463415

Katie Morag, the wee scamp from the Isle of Struay never fails to delight. There is to be a wedding on the island and everyone is excited. Except, that is, Grannie Island. It is Katie Morag's job to cheer her up before the big day.

WHERE'S SPOT?

Eric Hill
Puffin pb £4.50 0140506500

Where's Spot? is a wonderful beginning to your child's reading. An early learning classic, it has flaps to lift on every page and satisfies the most inquisitive mind.

Excellent Extras

Jane Hissey has now written 7 charming picture books about Old Bear and his friends. Old Bear actually exists and was a present from Jane's Grandmother.

OLD BEAR
Jane Hissey
Red Fox pb £3.99 0099554402
Old Bear and his friends need little introduction. The books of Old Bear, Bramwell Brown, Rabbit, Monkey and the others will delight children with their lifelike illustrations and warm stories.

THE STORY OF THE LITTLE MOLE WHO KNEW IT WAS NONE OF HIS BUSINESS
Werner Holzwarth
David Bennett pb £3.99
1856021017
This is not a story for the faint-hearted! Mole needs to find out who is responsible for dropping its 'business' on his head. He asks all the animals until he gets help from the flies. A strange introduction to the inner workings of nature and children will love it!

HONEY BISCUITS
Meredith Hooper
Kingfisher pb £4.99
0753402890
This picture book combines story with practical cooking. Ben is making biscuits with his Gran and she tells him where all the ingredients come from so that they can be used at home. The recipe for the biscuits is at the back so that you can make your own.

TATTYBOGLE
Sandra Horn and Ken Brown
Hodder pb £4.99 0340656778
Tattybogle the scarecrow loves watching the seasons pass. One autumn he gets blown away by the wind until only the stick is left. What will happen to him now?

Shirley Hughes

Shirley Hughes is a well-loved author for 3-5 year olds and has been for many years. She tells stories easily recognised by toddlers and has a very distinctive style of illustration.

ALFIE'S FEET
Shirley Hughes
Red Fox pb £3.50 0099256061
Alfie is a wonderful first hero whose antics with his new shoes are familiar and funny. Little sister Annie Rose is a great side-kick.

OUT AND ABOUT THROUGH THE YEAR
Shirley Hughes
Walker pb £6.99
0744560624
Gentle illustrations and poems introduce children to the changes of the seasons throughout the year.

ROSIE'S WALK
Pat Hutchins
Puffin pb £3.99 0140500324
An enjoyable and amusing story about a hen who takes a walk and unwittingly leads a fox, who is following her, into one disaster after another. A perfect first book. Also available in board book.

John Burningham

John Burningham's first book was published in 1963. Since then he has written many other favourite picture books. Now find out what his favourites were when he was little.

Author by author

When I was little it was World War II and we moved a lot around the English countryside, much of the time was spent living in a caravan which was often on a very remote farm. I remember being read to in the caravan with the sound of the rain thumping on the tin roof. My favourite story was called 'Mr Tickle's Caravan', illustrated by Cecil Aldin, it was about a man who had a magic handkerchief. I liked Rupert Bear but I was less keen on Beatrix Potter as it was too sad. When I finally learned to read myself my favourite book was an adventure called Brendon Chase about three boys who ran away from school and lived in the woods. To this day I think the illustrations by BB (Denys Watkins Pitchford) are some of the finest that portray the English countryside.

Some books by John Burningham:

Granpa
Avocado Baby
Courtney
Oi! Get Off Our Train
Cloudland
Whadyamean
(Spring 1999)
all published by Jonathan
Cape and Red Fox

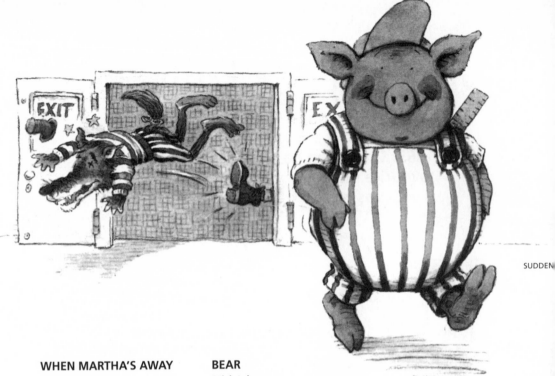

SUDDEN

WHEN MARTHA'S AWAY
Bruce Ingman
Mammoth pb £4.99
0749729570
In a lovely twist on the saying 'while the cat's away..' Lionel the cat tells us exactly what he gets up to while his owner is out. Just when you thought all that cats do is sleep...

Mick Inkpen

Mick Inkpen's illustrations and stories are full of warmth and wit. The comic toddler-like antics and charm of Kipper and Wibbly Pig have made him a favourite.

BEAR
Mick Inkpen
Hodder pb £4.99 0340698306
A bear falls out of the sky and into Sophie's playpen. It's a real bear not a toy bear and the children decide to hide it at home. Should they be allowed to keep it? There's a big surprise for you at the end!

LITTLE KIPPER
Mick Inkpen
Hodder pbs £3.50
There are now Kipper books for younger children. Smaller in size they are better for little hands to hold. Still with all the same charm they have a simple story line and the usual lovely pictures. Follow

Kipper as he gives a gosling a bath, builds sandcastles and tries to find the right toy for Arnold the pig.

THREADBEAR
Mick Inkpen
Hodder pb £4.99 0340573503
There is only one thing that has always been wrong with Threadbear – in his tummy is a squeaker that has never squeaked. However, with a little help from Father Christmas (and a trip to the land where the squeaker tree grows), he is soon on the road to recovery.

THE HUGE BAG OF WORRIES
Virginia Ironside
Macdonald pb £4.99
0750021241

Jenny has always been happy. But one day a worry comes along and is quickly followed by another until there are enough to fill a huge bag which Jenny carries everywhere with her. What can she do with these worries, who can she tell and will they ever go away? This is a reassuring book for children who sometimes feel anxious.

DEAR GREENPEACE
Simon James
Walker Books pb £3.99
0744530601

The story is told in letters written to Greenpeace about a whale in the garden pond. Full of imagination and humour, with clear illustrations which will appeal to the under fives.

LEON AND BOB
Simon James
Walker pb £4.99
0744554918

Leon's father is away and his mother is often busy. But he is not lonely because he has his friend, Bob. Except that Bob is imaginary. A reassuring story and a good reminder to occupied parents.

HAROLD AND THE PURPLE CRAYON
Crockett Johnson
Bloomsbury hb £5.99
0747532036

Harold decides to go for a walk one evening and as he goes he fills in the scene using his purple crayon. Adventure goes hand in hand with imagination to create this charming classic story.

Excellent Extras
Judith Kerr
- Mog is one of Judith Kerr's own cats
- The Tiger who Came to Tea was written 31 Years ago in 1968!

THE TIGER WHO CAME TO TEA
Judith Kerr
Collins pb £4.50 0006640613

For over 30 years children have been enthralled and delighted by this fanciful tale of a tiger joining a little girl and her mum for tea one day. Funny and entertaining.

MOG THE FORGETFUL CAT
Judith Kerr
Collins pb £4.50 0006640621

Mog is the kind of cat children everywhere will love. She's big, fat and forgetful and is a nuisance around the house till one day she surprises everyone by inadvertently stopping a burglar.

SHEEP IN WOLVES' CLOTHING
Satoshi Kitamura
Red Fox pb £4.50 0099610817

A group of trusting sheep leave their coats on the beach while they swim in the sea. Some cunning golf-playing wolves steal the coats and disappear. Cousin Elliott the Private Detective is brought in to try to catch the wolves. This is all told in Kitamura's distinctive, quirky style and provides a mad adventure.

CHARLIE'S CHECKLIST
Rory S. Lerman, Illustrated by Alison Bartlett
Macmillan pb £3.99
0333653106

Charlie the puppy wants to move from the country to a big city. He advertises for an owner. But Charlie is very fussy and has a long list of conditions. Maybe home is where the heart is.

THE MAN WHOSE MOTHER WAS A PIRATE
Margaret Mahy, illustrated Margaret Chamberlain
Puffin pb £3.99 0140506241

The off-beat and original tale of the little man, Sam, and his pirate mother who against all good advice travel with a wheelbarrow and a kite to see the sea. Vibrantly illustrated.

David Pelham

David Pelham has received wide acclaim for his 3-dimensional novelty books which entertain both children and adults alike.

Author by author

I was born in the grey drab days of the late thirties. My earliest memory was formed within a black, high sided, iron-framed hospital bed, attended by nurses in grey uniforms and doctors in white coats. One dark day I was visited by a tall gaunt uncle in a grey suit. With a wide cadaverous smile he reached deep into his big black attache case and slowly withdrew the most dazzling, most wonderful thing I had ever seen.

It was a magical clockwork butterfly, its tin wings painted in bright shining rainbow colours. It was the toymost toy imaginable, joyful and strange, wings flapping, colours merging, clockwork poetry flitting noisily about upon my bed tray as the dark clouds of war were gathering outside.

The memory of my wonderful tin butterfly, and all the stimulation it gave me as an infant, remains so vivid, that even after half a century, something of the joy of those memories is built into every children's book I create. It was the toy-like, magical quality of pop-up books that first attracted me to paper engineering, and now I strive to make my books for the young as stimulating as my butterfly was for me. My books are toys that can be read.

I WANT TO BE

GUESS HOW MUCH I LOVE YOU

Sam McBratney, illustrated by Anita Jeram
Walker hb £9.99
0744532248

Big and Little Nutbrown Hare discover how hard it is to measure their love for each other. A gentle story which has become a modern classic.

I LOVE BOATS

Flora McDonnell
Walker pb £5.99
0744543738

Flora McDonnell's big, detailed pictures make this a special picture book. Different boats and their jobs are colourfully illustrated and there is endless scope for the imagination.

ELMER

David McKee
Red Fox pb £4.50 0099697203

Elmer the patchwork elephant loves playing tricks on his fellow elephants. McKee achieves his striking look with bright, simple colours and a bold sense of fun.

CHARLOTTE'S PIGGY BANK

David McKee
Red Fox pb £4.99 0099721813

Charlotte is given a magic piggy bank and it will grant her a wish if she saves enough money. There is a terrible twist in this tale. Look out for all the extra things happening in the pictures as you read.

NOT NOW BERNARD

David McKee
Red Fox pb £4.50 0099240505

There's a real sting in this tale when trusting Bernard gets eaten by a monster, much to his parents' indifference. Recommended reading for those who believe children should be seen and not heard!

Colin McNaughton

Colin McNaughton writes funny picture books which are not unlike comic strips. They are full of great characters and can be laughed at again and again.

FOOTBALL CRAZY

Colin McNaughton
Mammoth pb £4.99
0749701250

There is a big match coming up with Leroy's Lions but Bruno is only the substitute for Tex's Tigers. He really wants the chance to play and show everyone what he can do. If only he could be the one to save the day.

SUDDENLY!

Colin McNaughton
Collins pb £4.99 0006645208

Preston Pig walked home from school and suddenly something nearly happened to him. Watch the wolf and laugh as he is ingeniously defeated every time.

SIX DINNER SID
Inga Moore
Macdonald pb £4.99
0750003049

Sid is a six-dinners-a-day kind
of cat. Therefore he lives not
only at number 1 Aristotle
Street, but at numbers, 2, 3,
4, 5 and 6 as well! None of his
six owners are aware of this as
they don't talk to each other,
but one day they find out!

PIG TROUBLE
**Barbara Mossmann and
Werner Farber**
Puffin pb £4.99 0140558934

Wild Pig can not believe it!
A strange pink thing with a
curly tail has arrived in his
wood- apparently it's a pig! It
is making itself at home and
stealing Wild Pig's friends
and it has to stop.

The Large Family

10 years ago Jill Murphy
created her Large family,
the elephants who have
all too human experiences.
A warm portrayal of
family life, they are
funny stories with often
farcical situations and a
realistic edge.

ALL IN ONE PIECE
Jill Murphy
Walker pb £3.99 0744509335

Mr and Mrs Large are trying
to get ready for the office
dinner dance. Their four
mischievous elephant children
however, are making it very
difficult for them to get out
of the house in one piece.
Murphy provides a warm and
humorous portrayal of family
life, instantly appealing to
children as well as to parents
who may find the situation
strangely familiar!

THE THREE LITTLE WOLVES
& THE BIG BAD PIG

MEG AND MOG
**Helen Nicoll
& Jan Pienkowski**
Puffin pb £3.99 0140501177
Since the early 1970's the
antics of inept witch, Meg and
her cat, Mog, have provided
bewitching entertainment.
The books, in bold colour,
encourage an affection for
the characters whilst
maintaining the fascination
of children for all things
witch-like.

WINNIE THE WITCH
Korky Paul & Valerie Thomas
Oxford UP pb £2.99
0192721976
A winner of the Children's
Book Award, this zanily
illustrated tale charts the
domestic problems (and their
resolution) of Winnie and her
cat. A great story, promoting
friendship and tolerance.

THE COMPLETE TALES OF
BEATRIX POTTER
Beatrix Potter
Frederick Warne hb £29.99
0723244049
Beatrix Potter's 23 tales and
verses are brought together
in one large format volume,
complete with her original
enchanting illustrations.
Arranged in the same order
as they were published, and
with an introductory note
which connects the real
places, people and animals in
her life with those in each
story, this is the perfect gift
for any Potter fan.

THE GREATEST SHOW
ON EARTH
John Prater
Walker pb £4.50
0744543592
This is one of the few books
for young children about
a circus. Everyone can do
amazing stunts except
Harry but maybe he does
have a role to play.
The detailed pictures
complement the story.

GOOD NIGHT, GORILLA
Peggy Rathman
Mammoth pb £4.50
0749723122
The zookeeper says goodnight
to the animals and thinks he
has tucked them up for the
night. But little does he know
that the mischievous gorilla is
following him and has a
different plan in mind.

LITTLE RABBIT FOO FOO
Michael Rosen
Walker pb £4.99
0744520657
Little Rabbit Foo Foo rides
through the forest scooping
up animals and bopping
them on the head. The good
fairy warns him to behave but
will he take any notice of her?

WE'RE GOING ON A
BEAR HUNT
**Michael Rosen,
illustrations Helen Oxenbury**
Walker Books pb £3.99
0744523230
A classic picture book for
under-sevens, demanding

participation from its
audience. "Swishy-swashy!
Splashy-splosh! Hoo Woo!"
bellows Rosen's loud and
boisterous text. Its wonderful
rhythm encourages you to
join in. Add to this Oxenbury's
lively watercolours and you
have a classic picture book.
Also available in board book.

I WANT TO BE
Tony Ross
Collins pb £4.99 0006643574
No one can fail to be
enchanted by the little
Princess who is wondering
how to be grown up.
Eventually the maid offers
the best advice. A story that
succeeds in suggesting what
is good and right in a
humorous way and
without moralising.

THE TRUE STORY OF THE
THREE LITTLE PIGS
**Jon Scieszka, illustrations
Lane Smith**
Puffin pb £3.99 0140540563
Superbly illustrated, this is
the big bad wolf's version
of the classic tale. He thinks
he got a rough deal and tells
you so in spoof Chandler
style. Smith's illustrations are
a rich dark combination of
oils and collage which create
a wonderful playground for
the imagination.

WHERE THE WILD THINGS ARE
Maurice Sendak
Collins pb £4.99 0006640869
'Where the Wild Things Are' tells the story of Max, who tames the wild things at night when he puts on his wolf suit and sails off in his boat. A reassuring story about how to overcome night fears, this is an award-winning, acknowledged children's classic.

THE WHALE'S SONG
Dyan Sheldon, illustrations Gary Blythe
Red Fox pb £4.50 0099737604
Lily believes her Grandmother's stories of the whales' singing, and one magical evening hears them for herself. A beautifully illustrated and atmospheric tale capturing the wonder of nature.

THE TOPSY-TURVIES
Francesca Simon, illustrations by Keren Ludlow
Dolphin pb £4.50 1858813328
This family do everything the wrong way round- or maybe it's the right way! The pictures light up this crazy, funny story.

WHAT'S THAT NOISE?
Francesca Simon and David Melling
Hodder pb £4.99 0340656735
Harry goes to stay at his Grandparents' house for the first time on his own. While he tries to get to sleep all kinds of strange noises disturb him and he calls for Grandpa who explains them all away. This will allay any fears of staying somewhere new.

THE THREE LITTLE WOLVES & THE BIG BAD PIG
Eugene Trivizas, illustrations Helen Oxenbury
Mammoth pb £3.99 0749725052
A wonderfully comic re-telling of the tale of the Three Little Pigs introducing new houses of concrete, plexiglas and...flowers! Enchanting illustrations.

THE VERY HUNGRY CATERPILL

BADGER'S PARTING GIFTS
Susan Varley
Collins pb £4.50 0006643175
Recommended by the Pre-School Playgroup Association, this moving story helps children to come to terms with the death of a loved one by treasuring their memories.

FROG IS FROG
Max Velthuijs
Andersen pb £4.99
0862648122
Frog wants to be able to do all the things that his friends do. It takes a while before he realises that they love him for the ordinary green frog that he is.

THE ELEPHANT AND THE BAD BABY
Elfrida Vipont
Puffin pb £3.99 0140500480
An elephant goes out for a walk and meets a bad baby. They embark on a 'rumpeting' run through town and one by one various members of the town give chase. Vipont uses rhythmic repetition in the best tradition of 'The Gingerbread Man' and 'The Enormous Turnip', making this a fun story to read aloud.

Martin Waddell

Martin Waddell writes picture books which tap into a child's mind with ease. They are both fun and emotive and they are always on subjects which children can relate to.

CAN'T YOU SLEEP, LITTLE BEAR?
Martin Waddell,
illustrations Barbara Firth
Walker pb £3.99 0744513162
Waddell has created a loveable, insomniac little bear that many will appreciate. A book that has become a classic, not least for its beautifully soothing illustrations.

YOU AND ME, LITTLE BEAR
Martin Waddell
illustrations Barbara Firth
Walker pb £4.99 0744554721
Little Bear wants to play but there are jobs to be done first. But if Little Bear helps Big Bear then maybe there will be time to have fun later... Another title in this charming bear series.

FARMER DUCK
Martin Waddell,
illustrations Helen Oxenbury
Walker pb £4.50 074453660X
The lazy farmer lounges in bed all day munching chocolate whilst down-trodden duck gets to do all the hard work - that is until the other animals hatch a plot to send him packing. Oxenbury's larger-than-life illustrations are glorious.

THE VELVETEEN RABBIT
Margery Williams
Mammoth pb £3.99
0749710551

The tale of the Velveteen Rabbit's life in the Nursery and his quest to become 'real'; the funny, sometimes sad, but always magical story of life as seen through the toy's eyes.

DR XARGLE'S BOOK OF EARTHLETS
**Jeanne Willis,
illustrations Tony Ross**
Red Fox pb £3.99 0099640104

Dr Xargle teaches his class of aliens about the weird and wonderful world of 'earthlets' (aka human babies). Zany and rib-tickling, this is one in a series of studies of all things strange from Earth.

HARRY THE DIRTY DOG
Gene Zion
Red Fox pb £4.50 0099978709

Harry hates having a bath but reconsiders one day when he is now so dirty that even his family can not recognise him. This is a classic well-loved story.

STORY COLLECTIONS

THE WALKER TREASURY OF FIRST STORIES
Walker hb £10.99
0744544475

A wonderful collection of thirty popular picture books, each with their original illustrations. Share stories or just browse through the pictures. Everyone will have their own favourite.

READ ME A STORY, PLEASE
Ed Wendy Cooling, illustrated by Penny Dann
Orion hb £20.00
1858815487

Fifty stories to read aloud. The old and new are combined to tell of princesses, giants, monsters and fairies. All the things you need in a collection of bedtime tales. The reader also has suggested durations in easy time-bites, 2, 5 or 10 minute tales. What a great idea!

MONKEY RUN

Young Readers

YOUNG READERS

Learning to read is a really exciting time; no longer are children so dependent on receiving stories told by others but can enjoy the wonderful experience of getting lost in a book themselves.

Reading at home and choosing your own stories to read plays a big part of sustaining the fun. It supplements any reading schemes that are being used at school and stops it becoming just another lesson in the day.

Ability varies considerably at this age but there are books available that will suit any child who is taking the first steps of reading for themselves.

To help we have split the following chapter into various sections. Picture books from the pre-school section will still be useful but we have chosen more involved picture books for older children who demand more from their stories. This is followed by first readers and then by longer stories where there are still a lot of pictures to break up the text. Lastly, there is a selection of stories for fluent readers with in-depth plots and characters.

The chapter will parallel the developments in a child's reading. It introduces many classic stories as well as excellent authors who write for other age groups and can help provide encouragement to move on to stories for older children.

Just because children have started reading by themselves it doesn't mean that they can't still enjoy picture books. In fact, they are an excellent way of adding confidence in reading as the format is still familiar. Here we have chosen a few exceptional picture books with more text, that children can try their new reading skills out on.

HORRID HENRY AND OTHER STORIES

Picture Books

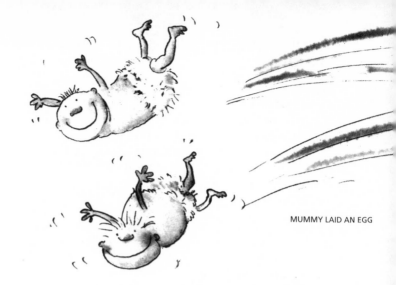

MUMMY LAID AN EGG

Picture books can still be enjoyed by children who have begun to read for themselves. In fact some are written and designed specially for an older age group. They provide reassurance as children are familiar with the larger format but have more text which younger readers can embark on themselves. Most of all they tell a child that reading books themselves can still be a great way of having fun.

IT WAS A DARK AND STORMY NIGHT
Janet & Allan Ahlberg
Puffin pb £5.99
0140545867
Antonio is kidnapped and forced to entertain his captors by telling them stories. The bandits won't be satisfied however, and they argue so much about the plots that Antonio manages to slip quietly home.

FOWL PLAY
Jonathan Allen
Dolphin pb £4.50 1858814316
Six prize chickens have gone missing and it is Hubert Hound's job to investigate. Everyone is questioned in turn and the pieces fall into place. The clues are slowly revealed so that you can try to work it out as well. The characterisation of the animals is brilliant.

Babette Cole's books are humorous and irreverent. They can span a wide age group and burst with energy. Children's books are her passion.

DR DOG
Babette Cole
Red Fox pb £4.99
0099650819
The Gumboyle's dog is a very clever doctor who can make anyone feel better and also takes the time to explain what made them ill in the first place. This is a great story with funny pictures and diagrams. Health education told in a crazy way.

MUMMY LAID AN EGG
Babette Cole
Red Fox pb £4.50 0099299119
When Mum and Dad try and tell the kids about the birds and the bees they get it all wrong. Luckily, their clever children set them straight. This hilarious guide to the facts of life is frank, factual and a good introduction for parents!

SOPHIE AND THE SEAWOLF
Helen Cresswell, illustrated by Jason Cockcroft
Hodder pb £4.99
0340682965
Sophie wants to hold the stars and for the sea to speak to her. One day the sea answers her in the form of a beautiful wolf who dares her to see the world through his eyes. An enchanting story.

THE ENORMOUS CROCODILE
Roald Dahl, illustrations Quentin Blake
Puffin pb £4.99 0140503420
A marvellous tale about a big bad crocodile who wants to eat 'juicy' and 'yummy' children for lunch but is foiled by the ingenious animals in the jungle. The witty text is complemented by the funny illustrations.
99

THE GIRAFFE, THE PELLY AND ME
Roald Dahl, illustrations Quentin Blake
Puffin pb £4.50 0140505660
The enthralling tale of the Ladderless Window Cleaning Company (giraffe, pelican and monkey) and their friend Billy, who together embark on the job of a lifetime: cleaning all 677 windows of the Duke of Hampshire's house, with spectacularly funny results.
99

DIRTY RATS
Richard Groves, illustrated by Rowan Barnes Murphy
Macdonald pb £4.99 0750022655
Lenox doesn't want to be a dirty rat; he wants to build rockets. But his sisters have other ideas. Terrible jokes in the story and the clever pictures make this gangster book a great story.

AMAZING GRACE
Mary Hoffman
Frances Lincoln pb £3.99 0711206996
Grace has a wonderfully wild imagination and loves to act out stories and dress up. When she wants to be Peter Pan in the school play and some of the other children try to discourage her, Ma and Grandma show her that she can be anything she wants to be.

BULLY
David Hughes
Walker pb £4.99 0744536243
A powerful exploration of playground bullying which tackles the problem in a bold, blunt, yet accessible manner.

JOLLY ROGER
Colin McNaughton
Walker pb £4.99 074451732X
Roger becomes a cabin-boy on a pirate ship and embarks upon a rumbustious romp across the high seas. This is an energetic cruise through pirate life, filled with jokes, curses and lots of yo-ho-hos!

WATCH OUT FOR THE GIANT-KILLERS!
Colin McNaughton
Walker pb £5.99 0744547776
A chance meeting between a small boy and a green giant in an equatorial rainforest leads to an amusing and extraordinary story of times when giants lived in Britain. This is a subtle thought-provoking book on conservation of the earth.

MISS JUMP THE JOCKEY

SASSY GRACIE

James Sage, illustrations Pierre Pratt
Macmillan pb £4.99
0333684281

Sassy Gracie has a pair of Big Red Shoes and they make her feel like dancing. One day, she has to cook a meal for an important guest and she dances to pass the time. But then she feels hungry and has a little taste of chicken. This is a rhythmic tale with quirky pictures.

BROTHER EAGLE SISTER SKY

Chief Seattle, illustrations Susan Jeffers
Puffin pb £4.99 014054514X

Nearly 150 years ago, Chief Seattle, a respected and peaceful leader of one of the North West Indian Nations, delivered a compelling speech warning of the dangers of destroying nature for future generations. Susan Jeffers' beautiful illustrations bring his words to life, creating a moving and powerful plea for conservation.

THE STINKY CHEESEMAN AND OTHER FAIRLY STUPID TALES

Jon Scieszka, illustrations Lane Smith
Puffin pb £4.99
0140548963

Full of wild creatures, bizarre ideas, mad typography and surreal images, this

Bully

reworking of old fashioned fairy tales is a classic. It stretches the barriers of what a picture book should be: Chicken Licken is even squashed by the table of contents!

MATHS CURSE

Jon Scieszka and Lane Smith
Puffin pb £4.99 0140563814

On Monday in maths Mrs Fibonacci says that almost everything can be thought of as a maths problem. From this the problems really do start. Time, measurements, even the dreaded fractions seem to be everywhere in everyday life. Could things be any worse?

HOORAY FOR DIFFENDOOFER DAY!

Dr Seuss, Jack Prelutsky and Lane Smith
Collins hb £9.99
0001720279

The strange teachers at Diffendoofer school teach weird and wacky things. Will it be enough to get the pupils through the test to keep the school open? Enter into another crazy rhyming world from Dr Seuss and also find out how this new book came to be.

HOW TO LIVE FOREVER

Colin Thompson
Red Fox £4.99 0099461811

Peter is determined to find the one missing book from the library that stores every book ever printed. The illustrations in this book are filled with amusing detail and dreadful puns but the poignant text is deceptively simple.

WATCH OUT FOR THE GIANT KILLERS

THE RASCALLY CAKE
Jeanne Willis and Korky Paul
Puffin pb £4.99
0140554726
Hilariously revolting verse. Mr O'Parsley only eats disgusting food and decides to make the most gruesome cake ever but things don't go according to plan.

First Readers

The first story books which can be tackled independently by children can be difficult to choose. A reading series is often a good introduction because the language and vocabulary are kept consistent even if the titles are by different authors. The following series offer good support to young readers.

FAVOURITE TALES
Ladybird hb £1.50 each
Over 30 popular fairy tales in attractive and affordable individual volumes. Consistent, easy-to-read texts and bright illustrations throughout. Titles include 'The Sleeping Beauty', 'Cinderella' and many others.

BEGINNER BOOKS
Dr. Seuss
Collins pb £3.50 each
Dr Seuss's ridiculous rhymes and absurd characters are a brilliant introduction to the richness of language. The illustrations are wacky and children love the zany humour. The best titles include 'Green Eggs and Ham', 'Hop on Pop', and the well-loved 'The Cat in the Hat'.
99

HAPPY FAMILIES
Allan Ahlberg
Puffin pb £3.50 each
A series of individual stories, ideal for bridging the gap between picture books and early readers. Based on the updated (more PC) characters from the card game, each story is full of slapstick humour set in identifiable and reassuring situations. Titles include 'Miss Jump the Jockey' and 'Mr Biff the Boxer'.
99

DAYS WITH FROG AND TOAD
Arnold Lobel
Mammoth I Can Read pb £4.99 0749711906
Frog and Toad are best friends and these short tales show how they have fun flying kites and telling stories to each other. This is a gentle beginner reader series with large, well-spaced type and simple, colour illustrations. There are also stories with Else Minarik's irresistible Little Bear which are illustrated by Sendak.

JETS SERIES
Collins B/W pb £3.50 each
colour £4.99 each
Lively stories with integral black and white illustrations, suitable for children gaining in reading confidence. Watch out for Bob Wilson, Colin West and Rose Impey titles. Some are also available in colour.

Moving On

As children need more from their books it is important not to overwhelm them. Lots of pictures are still comforting, and colour ones are often best, but the use of language can afford to be a bit more advanced. It is a good idea to check that the chapter lengths are short so that the child can have a sense of achievement as they read. The following titles are from various series to introduce you to individual stories which may appeal.

THE MAGNIFICENT MUMMIES
Tony Bradman
Mammoth Blue Bananas pb £3.99
0749727675
This series serves as a valuable transition from picture books to reading stories. Bright illustrations and just enough text provide satisfying reads for young children. This amusing story stars the Mummy family and their Mummy cat.

CARE OF HENRY
Anne Fine
Walker pb £3.50 0744552583
Hugo has to choose who will look after him when his Mum goes into hospital to have her baby. Food, baths and television are top of his list. But how Henry, his dog, will be cared for is the most important question.

TAKING THE CAT'S WAY HOME
Jan Mark
Walker pb £3.50 0744536677
William is the new boy at school and he does not like Jane or her cat, Furlong. He is turning the other boys against her too, and they are going to get Jane after school. The only way to escape is to go along the wall but only Furlong knows the way.

DOG ON A BROOMSTICK
Jan Page
Corgi Pups pb £3.50
0552545384
Who ever heard of a witch's dog? But this witch is desperate: her cat has run off to test cat food and she needs to win the Grand Spell Contest. The dog will have to do. This is one of a gentle series of first storybooks.

GORILLA GRANNY
Frank Rodgers
Macdonald pb £3.99
0750023570
This is a yellow spined storybook which is ideal for reading aloud or alone with company. Gus the Gorilla runs away from the zoo and Suzie is determined to disguise him. Macdonald do red spined storybooks for more confident readers.

THE JEALOUS GIANT
Kaye Umansky
First Young Puffin pb £3.99
0140388400
Hetty is a wrestler and she has a new trainer. But now she doesn't have time to cook for Waldo and take care of his every need. Waldo needs a plan to win her back.

THE DINOSAUR'S PACKED LUNCH
Jacqueline Wilson
Corgi Pups pb £3.50
0552528188
Dinah goes on a school trip to see the dinosaurs. Surprisingly, one of them comes to life and gives her some lunch. That night very strange things begin to happen...

More Developed Stories

These books are ideal to share with any child between the ages of 5 and 8 but are much more advanced to read independently. There are generally fewer pictures and the chapters are longer. Some of the following books have a number of illustrations but the text is quite challenging.

THE RAILWAY CAT
Phyllis Arkle
Puffin pb £3.25 0140316604
Hack, the new railway porter, doesn't like cats and has plans to get rid of Alfie, the railway cat. Alfie's fight back is funny and action-packed.

,,

HARRY THE POISONOUS CENTIPEDE
Lynne Reid Banks
Collins Red Storybook pb £3.99
0006751970
Harry may be poisonous but he's an attractive little centipede. This is about his adventures with George as they disregard all warnings and enter the above ground world of the scary Hoo-Mins.

,,

SIMON AND THE WITCH
Margaret Stuart Barry
Collins pb £2.99 006720641
Is Simon's best friend really a witch? She is certainly cantankerous enough. Just wait until Simon begins to learn a few spells too!

MS WIZ SPELLS TROUBLE
Terence Blacker
Macmillan pb £2.50
0330310968
When feminist witch Ms Wiz takes over Class Three, strange things start to happen which have outrageously comic results.

HURRICANE BETSY
Malorie Blackman
Mammoth pb £2.99
0749714239
There are explosively funny results when Betsy decides to pre-empt the approaching hurricane with her own kind of storm. A lively story set in an evocative Caribbean background.

,,

PADDINGTON
Michael Bond
Collins pb £3.50 000670428X
The classic story of the marmalade-eating bear who gets into endless embarrassing scrapes.

,,

DILLY THE DINOSAUR
Tony Bradman
Mammoth pb £2.99
0749703660
The first book about Dilly, the naughtiest dinosaur in the world who gets even naughtier when he doesn't get his own way.

MILLY-MOLLY-MANDY
Joyce Lankester Brisley
Kingfisher hb £9.99
1856974936
The book about the girl with the short hair, short legs and short frocks! Well-loved and still absolutely delightful, her traditional and charming adventures have been enjoyed since the 1920's. This is a lovely facsimile edition of the original stories.

FLAT STANLEY
Jeff Brown, illustrations Tomi Ungerer
Mammoth pb £2.99
0749701374
Stanley Lambchop suddenly finds himself to be an inch thick when a bulletin board falls on him. This leads to endless possibilities – squeezing under doors, being posted in envelopes and slipping down drains. Illustrated amusingly throughout.

,,

GHOST GOALIE
J.Burchett
Bloomsbury pb £3.99
0747538468
First in the series about the Tiger football team. This is an exciting series for those who are gaining confidence with their reading. The Tigers need to win the tournament and, with their coach ill, help comes from an unusual person.

THE JULIAN STORIES
Ann Cameron
Transworld pb £2.99
0440863333
A collection of six lively tales in which Julian gets into plenty of mischief, and explores the trials and tribulations of family life and childhood friendship.

MR MAJEIKA
Humphrey Carpenter
Puffin pb £3.50 0140316779
The first in a series of books about the teacher with the flying carpet and his magic ways of dealing with trouble makers. A fun and entertaining book for children who have developed confidence and reading fluency.
"

THE BIG ... SERIES
Rob Childs
Transworld pb £2.50
An action-packed series following the adventures of two football-mad brothers. You don't have to be a football fan to enjoy these realistic and fast-moving stories full of sporting action.

HAMISH
W.J. Corbett
Hodder pb £2.99 0340619546
Hamish is a mountain goat. Unfortunately he is terrified of climbing mountains. Every day he makes an excuse to stay behind. The other goats have lost all respect for him and now he is a laughing stock. The chance does come to prove himself and maybe Hamish will be brave enough to rise to the occasion.

A GIFT FROM WINKLESEA
Helen Cresswell
Puffin pb £3.25 0140304932
Dan and his sister Mary find the ideal present for their mother at the seaside. The egg-shaped stone sits proudly on the mantelpiece until it hatches the Gift – and plenty of fun ensues.

THE MAGIC FINGER
Roald Dahl
Puffin pb £3.50 0140341625
The delightful tale of one girl's magic finger and the punishment it can deliver to those who make her angry. Wittily told and with a strong environmental theme.
"

FANTASTIC MR FOX
Roald Dahl
Puffin pb £3.50 0140326715
Mr Fox outwits the mean farmers Bunce, Boggis and Bean, with traditional Dahl flair. An action-filled adventure full of subversive humour.
"

AMBER BROWN IS NOT A CRAYON
Paula Danziger
Macmillan pb £2.99 0330331434
Amber's best friend Daniel is moving to a new town and they both have to work out how to cope with changes. An imaginative book full of gentle humour and observation.
"

HORRID HENRY AND OTHER STORIES

THE UNSINKABLE TITANIC
Andrew Donkin
Macdonald pb £4.50
0750024798
As Sarah delights in this huge, beautiful ship little does she know what the future holds. This series of storybooks provide exciting stories and thorough historical information for younger children.

MY NAUGHTY LITTLE SISTER
Dorothy Edwards
Mammoth pb £3.99
0749700548
Classic stories of the spirited, naughty little sister and her cohort Bad Harry. A gentle and reassuring look at misbehaviour.

HOW TO WRITE REALLY BADLY
Anne Fine
Mammoth pb £3.99
0749720239
Two schoolboys discover hidden talents while they work on a project. As with Anne Fine's many other stories, this is very funny, yet has something to say about how we and others see ourselves.

"

BILL'S NEW FROCK
Anne Fine
Mammoth pb £2.99
0582095565
Bill Simpson wakes up one morning to find out that he is a girl and is forced to go to school in a frilly pink dress. A brilliant and funny observation of the differences between boys and girls.

"

Excellent Extras
Many of Pat Hutchins' books have been influenced by her two sons. Titch was written for her elder son Morgan, and Sam, complaining of not having his own book, had 'Happy Birthday Sam' written for him. 'The House that Sailed Away' stars their whole family including Grandma and their cat!!

FOLLOW THAT BUS
Pat Hutchins
Red Fox pb £2.99 0099932202
Class 6 should be going on an ordinary school trip until its absent-minded teacher switches her bag. The story becomes a fast-paced cops and robbers chase, making it a trip they will never forget!

"

VLAD THE DRAC
Ann Jungman
Collins pb £2.99 0006732720
Paul and Judy don't realise what they have let themselves in for when they take home a vampire as a holiday souvenir.

"

FANTASTIC MR FO

Dick King-Smith

Dick King-Smith writes stories for all ages. They usually have an animal setting; children with pets or animals as the main characters. Although they often contain analogies to human life his books can always be approached on two levels which makes them accessible to everyone.

ALL BECAUSE OF JACKSON
Dick King-Smith
Corgi pb £2.99
0552528218
Jackson is a rabbit with a dream; he wants to go to sea. With his girlfriend Bunny he stows away on a ship. This is the tale of how rabbits first arrived in Australia and colonised it for themselves.

BLESSU & DUMPLING
Dick King-Smith
Puffin pb £3.25 0140346988
Blessu is an elephant with a problem – he gets hayfever! Sneezing so much makes his trunk stretch and stretch in this gentle story.

SOPHIE SERIES
Dick King-Smith
Walker pb £3.50
Sophie is a wonderful creation from a master storyteller. She is witty, resourceful and imaginative as she gathers experience with animals to realise her dream of becoming a lady farmer. Begin the series with 'Sophie's Snail'.

MY BEST FIEND
Sheila Lavelle
Puffin pb £3.50 0140371826
The first in the popular 'fiend' series. The 'fiend' is Angela, Charlie's best friend. Angela gets long-suffering Charlie into all sorts of scrapes and mishaps. This funny book is a collection of dreadful deeds by two 'sweet' girls.

PRACTICALLY PERFECT
Hilary McKay
Hodder pb £3.50 0340655747
Things are difficult at the palace. It is decided at a secret meeting that life would be much easier if the Queen could be married off. But it is going to be far from easy as the Queen is fussy and needs her Prince to be practically perfect!

Bel Mooney

Bel Mooney has now written 10 stories about Kitty the lovable but mischievous heroine who goes through all the usual problems and questioning of a young child. They are based on her own daughter- also called Kitty!

I DON'T WANT TO
Bel Mooney
Mammoth pb £3.99
0749704209
'I don't want to clean my teeth', 'I don't want to eat my vegetables'. There are lots of things Kitty doesn't want to do but being stubborn leads to problems, and in the end Kitty finds that saying 'yes', rather than 'no', isn't so bad after all.

RED EYES AT NIGHT
Michael Morpurgo
Hodder Read Alone pb £3.50
0340687533
Nobody will fail to identify with this rivalry story. Millie hates Geraldine and only one thing keeps boastful Geraldine quiet – a red-eyed ghost!

99

THE DANCING BEAR
Michael Morpurgo
Collins pb £2.99 0006745113
In a small mountain village, orphaned Roxanne finds an abandoned bear cub, and soon they are inseparable. The day comes however, when Roxanne must leave the village and her bear. A deeply moving story told with great charm.
"

STINKERBELL
J.J Murhall
Bloomsbury pb £3.99 0747525110
Stinkerbell is a very smelly fairy who lives at the bottom of the garden. Outrageous, bad, cheeky but lovable. She is desperate to show the other fairies that she can rescue Douglas and the royal baby from the terrible Gobs.
"

THE WORST WITCH
Jill Murphy
Puffin pb £3.50 0140311084
Mildred Hubble is a trainee witch at Miss Cackle's Academy for Witches and is the worst pupil in the whole school! The first in a hugely popular series about school life with a difference.

JOSIE SMITH
Magdalen Nabb
Collins pb £2.99 0006737447
The first book about Josie, her adventures and her understanding mother. These stories capture the child's world perfectly and gently unravel confusing childhood problems.
"

THE ENCHANTED HORSE
Magdalen Nabb
Collins pb £2.99 0006747213
Lonely and unhappy Irina is not looking forward to Christmas. Then she sees a shabby wooden horse in a junk shop and chooses it for her Christmas present, with magical consequences.
"

THE OWL TREE
Jenny Nimmo
Walker pb £3.50 0744554004
Granny Diamond loves the owl-tree at the bottom of her garden. Unfortunately, Mr Rock hates it and it is his tree. He wants to cut it down and so Joe sets out to find out why. But is he brave enough?
"

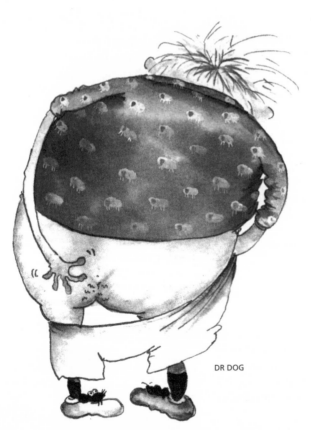

DR DOG

Bags I the pearls

IT WAS A DARK AND STORMY NIGHT

THE IT DOESN'T MATTER SUIT
Sylvia Plath
Faber pb £3.99 057119060X
Little Max Nix lives with his large family and dreams of having a suit. Not just any old suit but a suit fine enough to do Everything in. One day a parcel arrives containing a brand new, mustard yellow suit. Who will get to wear it?

MRS PEPPERPOT STORIES
Alf Proysen
Red Fox pb £3.99 0099141213
Endearing tales of an old woman who shrinks to the size of a pepperpot at the most inconvenient moments. Plenty of humour and wit have kept these books popular for nearly 30 years.

THE GINGER NINJA
Shoo Rayner
Hodder Read Alone pb £2.99 0340619554
The Ginger Ninja stories are a funny series of first stories about the cat who has a magical collar which turns him into a cat to be reckoned with!

THE DAY THE SMELLS WENT WRONG
Catherine Sefton
Puffin pb £2.99 0140370714
One day Jackie and Phil wake up to find that everything has changed its smell and the Chief Inspector of Smells needs help fast. A good story for children just starting to read on their own.

Colin McNaughton

Colin was born in Tyneside and didn't like school at all. After a stint in community theatre he decided to go to art school. Then starts the success story. When he left art school many years later all of his degree show was made up of published work. Children love his books for their energy and humour. Find out below what his influences have been.

Author by author

"Mr. McNaughton, do you ever write serious books?" a six year old asked me the other day.

"Nope." said I, "The world is a miserable enough place as it is without me adding to it."

As a child I was bored witless with reading schemes. Dull plodding texts with wooden, charmless illustrations.

I sought refuge in my comics : story-lines full of awful puns, drawings bursting with energy. My favourite artist/writer was Dudley D. Watkins. His best character – 'Oor Wullie'. Daft as a bucket in the Sunday Post.

British comics, mixed with the American ones that were flooding Britain in the fifties were where I learnt to draw and tell stories. I simply spend each day in my studio trying to recapture that wonderful sense of 'letting go' I felt when I was a child whenever I opened a comic and joined forces with the words and pictures.

Now, I make my own comics. People call them 'picture books' – same difference.

HOWL!

Francesca Simon

Francesca went to university in Britain and in America and has been a journalist, but now she devotes her time to writing children's books. One of her characters, Horrid Henry was 'born' like this.

Author by author

When I was a child growing up in California all I ever did was read. (I did sometimes go to the beach, but usually I just read – comics, myths, fairy tales, novels.) My favourite authors were Beverly Cleary, who wrote the Ramona and Henry Huggins books, Louisa May Alcott, Andrew Lang (The Orange Book of Fairy Tales) and Edward Eager (Half-Magic). Once I was so engrossed in Half-Magic that I didn't even notice that my class had left the library.

I enjoy writing about rebellious children like Horrid Henry, probably because I was usually well-behaved. I'm often asked if Horrid Henry comes from 'real life'. The initial ideas, such as tricking the tooth fairy, dealing with nits, or trying to earn money – in Henry's case by selling Perfect Peter as a slave to Moody Margaret! – are mainly sparked by the concerns of my eight year old son Joshua, and then given a 'horrid' twist. Henry himself is the imp inside everyone.

Some titles by Francesca Simon

Horrid Henry
Horrid Henry And The Secret Club
Horrid Henry And The Tooth Fairy
Horrid Henry Strikes It Rich
Horrid Henry's Nits

all published by Orion

HORRID HENRY AND OTHER STORIES
Francesca Simon
Orion pb £2.99 1858810701
Henry is every teacher's troublemaker and every parent's nightmare. Henry is utterly horrid. He shouts and screams and stomps his way through four separate stories. But does he get his come-uppance in the end and is he a match for Moody Margaret?

CLEVER POLLY AND THE STUPID WOLF
Catherine Storr
Puffin pb £2.99 014130312X
One great big hungry wolf meets one rather small girl. Yet Polly manages not only to escape from the wolf's clutches; she also successfully turns around this traditional tale by outwitting the stupid animal again and again in a series of bedtime-sized chapters.

"

KARATE PRINCESS
Jeremy Strong
Puffin pb £3.25 0140328041
Another fairy tale is turned upside-down when Princess Belinda Stormbelly is around. Her father thinks that she'll never find a husband. However Belinda is an extraordinary young lady with some very funny ideas of her own!

THE HUNDRED-MILE-AN-HOUR DOG
Jeremy Strong, illustrated by Nick Sharratt
Puffin pbk £3.99 0140380302
Trevor has an untrainable dog, Streaker. This is a mad story of their adventures. A huge favourite.

"

THE OWL WHO WAS AFRAID OF THE DARK
Jill Tomlinson
Mammoth pb £2.99 074970795X
Plop, the baby barn owl, is afraid of the dark, but everyone he meets has reasons for liking the night and gradually Plop realises that the dark isn't so bad after all. This wonderful, reassuring book has proved to be a modern classic.

"

QUEEN VICTORIA'S SWING
Karen Wallace
Collins Red Storybook £2.99 0006752195
At the fair Amanda and Clare climb into a Victorian swingboat and climb out at Windsor castle in 1854! They are even more surprised when they make two friends who tell them that their mother is the Queen.

LITTLE WOLF'S BOOK OF BADNESS
Ian Whybrow, illustrations Tony Ross
Collins pb £4.50 0006751601
Little Wolf has to go to Cunning College for Brute Beasts to learn the nine Rules of Badness from Uncle Bigbad. His letters home make this an entertaining story; the ideas are inspired.

"

GOBBOLINO THE WITCH'S CAT
Ursula Moray Williams
Puffin pb £3.99 0140302395
Born a witch's cat, Gobbolino doesn't want to be one. The story follows his search for a new home and a happy ending.

"

FAIRY TALES AND MYTHOLOGY

Fairy Tales has become the generic term for the oral tradition of Europe. They are tales of ordinary people and their imaginations. Far more than just stories for children they are an invaluable way of looking at traditions of morality, humour and heroism in history. They also continue to be used throughout literature in many other guises.

The myths and legends in this section will be enjoyed by younger children to share or older children to read alone. The books are age-ranged for the style and complexity of the language . This provides guidance but different children respond differently to different texts.

There are classic editions of myths and fairy tales, some highly illustrated, some not. There are also some modern re-tellings for those who like an extra twist in a familiar tale. Become absorbed in these fantastic stories.

FAIRY TALES BY TERRY JONES

THE NURSERY STORYBOOK
Georgie Adams
Dolphin pb £6.99 1858816394
This is an enchanting first collection of 8 fairy tales with lively pictures. It's ideal to share or read alone and includes all the familiar tales.
4-6
"

AESOP'S FABLES
Ladybird £1.75 0721417574
5-8
"

AESOP'S FABLES
Puffin pb £3.99 0140369848
9-12

THE VERY BEST OF AESOP'S FABLES
Margaret Clark, illustrations Charlotte Voake
Walker pb £5.99 0744531497
5-8

FAIRY TALES
Hans Christian Andersen, illustrations Lisbeth Zwerger
Ragged Bears hb £14.95
0887081827
An outstanding gift edition of classic Andersen tales, illustrated in gentle, evocative watercolours to match the delicate prose.

THE SWAN'S STORIES
Hans Christian Andersen, translated by Brian Alderson
Walker hb £12.99
0744532981
The main characters in these stories are not people. Ordinary household objects like pots and pans become the heroes in this beautiful collection of Andersen's lesser known tales.
7-9

THE WILLOW PATTERN STORY
Allan Drummond
Ragged Bears pb £3.99
1558584137
The pattern is so famous and yet it is unusual to find the story in picture format for children. Drummond retells the story using the china pattern as a basis for his illustrations.
5-8

ANANCY & MR DRYBONE
Fiona French
Frances Lincoln pb £3.99
0711207879
Prizewinning illustrator Fiona French creates an original story based on characters from traditional Caribbean and West African folktales. Both poor Anancy and rich Mr Dry-Bone want to marry the beautiful Miss Louise but she will only marry a man who can make her laugh. A superb interweaving of text and pictures.
5-9

BOOK OF CREATION STORIES

THE BROTHERS GRIMM GRIMM'S FAIRY TALES
Jacob and Wilhelm Grimm
Puffin pb £3.99
0140366962
The Grimm brothers began their record early last century in Germany. They have immortalised many familiar tales such as 'Hansel and Gretel' and 'Snow White'.
9-12

THE SONG OF THE EARTH
Mary Hoffman and Jane Ray
Dolphin pb £6.99 1858813417
The four elements are explored in myths and traditions from around the world and in the natural phenomena that effect the earth. The rich illustrations make this a really magical and interesting book.
7-10

SEASONS OF SPLENDOUR
Madhur Jaffrey
Puffin pb £4.99 0140346996
This is the best version of traditional tales from India available. Mainly based on the Hindu epics, it is beautifully illustrated by Michael Foreman.
9-12

Excellent Extras
The word myth comes from an ancient Greek word 'mythos' which means a spoken or written story.

FAIRY TALES
Terry Jones, illustrations Michael Foreman
Puffin pb £4.99 0140322620
Thirty new fairy tales full of fantasy from the ex-Monty Python member. Exciting and enthralling adventures with a host of magical characters make this a collection of modern classics, great for shared reading and ideal for reading aloud.

BOOK OF MYTHOLOGY
Kingfisher pb £9.99
0753402572
This book provides a comprehensive look at world mythology; there are gods, goddesses and heroes from all around the world. Fascinating introductions to different civilisations firmly place the myths in their contexts. The presence of an easy to use index and glossary and rich illustrations make this an invaluable reference book.
9-12

THE PUFFIN CLASSICS MYTHS & LEGENDS
Roger Lancelyn Green
Puffin pb £3.99 – 4.99
Amongst the Puffin Classics series are inspired retellings of myths and legends. Roger Lancelyn Green's concise prose makes sense of the vast complexity of the Greek Myths and the stories of the Trojan Wars and his enthusiasm invigorates the narrative. His tales of King Arthur are drawn from many sources, the most obvious being Malory, whose mood and poetry are echoed both in the language and the woodcuts which illustrate the text. These stories are full of excitement and drama.
9-12

STORY OF KING ARTHUR
Robin Lister
Kingfisher pb £6.99
086272970X
Robin Lister draws on a wide variety of sources as he unfolds the famous stories of King Arthur and his Round Table, of the doomed love of Lancelot and Guinevere, of the quest for the Holy Grail and Arthur's final defeat and departure for the magical Isle of Avalon. Alan Baker's evocative illustrations complement the text perfectly.
9-12

BOOK OF CREATION STORIES
Margaret Mayo, illustrations Louise Brierley
Orchard hb £12.99 1852137746
A wonderful collection of stories from around the world which reveals the ways different cultures have explained how and why things began. Mayo's ten retellings are delightful to read alone, the text is clear enough for quite new readers, and even better to read aloud. Each story is complemented by illustrations which are soft and magical yet full of colour and vibrancy.
7-12

FIRST FAIRY TALES
Margaret Mayo, illustrations Selina Young
Orchard Books pb £8.99
1852135514
Nine favourite fairy tales re-told in rhyme and with repetition especially for young children. Ideal for reading aloud and great for shared reading, this collection is illustrated in bright, cheerful full-colour illustrations and contains classic tales such as Snow White and the Seven Dwarfs,

Hansel and Gretel and Cinderella.
5-8

THE ORCHARD BOOK OF MYTHICAL BIRDS AND BEASTS

Margaret Mayo and Jane Ray
Orchard hb £12.99 1852137541
Discover the stories behind amazing creatures in mythology. The book includes the unicorn, phoenix and many more unusual tales from around the world.
6+

CELTIC MYTHS

Sam McBratney
Macdonald hb £12.99
0750018135
This is a retelling of stories from English, Irish, Scottish and Welsh folklore. It is an unusual collection and includes a lesser known legend of King Arthur. All the tales are exciting and full of adventure.
9-12

ONE THOUSAND AND ONE ARABIAN NIGHTS

Geraldine McCaughrean
Oxford UP pb £5.99
019274500X
This is an original version re-written especially for children but still in the traditional style. All the stories are linked by the love-story of Shahrazad and her king and make compelling reading for older children.
9-12

ORCHARD MYTHS SERIES

Geraldine McCaughrean and Tony Ross
Orchard hb £4.99
These are the best known Greek myths for first readers with lots of pictures and clear text. These titles make sure that these often exciting adventures are available for children to discover for themselves. Look out as well for the range on Creation Myths.
5-8

ORCHARD BOOK OF GREEK MYTHS

Geraldine McCaughrean
Orchard hb £10.99 1852133732
This volume includes the famous adventures of Jason, Theseus and Odysseus and also less well-known tales such as the story of Arachne the spinner who boasted of her prowess and was turned into a spider by the gods. Lively text with appealing illustrations.
6+
99

ROBIN OF SHERWOOD

Michael Morpurgo,
Illustrations Michael Foreman
Hodder pb £8.99 0340690143
This is an atmospheric and compelling retelling of Robin Hood. It is impossible not to be immersed in the Outcasts' adventures and with Foreman's pictures to spur on the imagination, the drama of the battles and emotion of the friendships become real.
9-12
99

SQUIDS WILL BE SQUIDS

Jon Scieszka, Illustrations
Lane Smith
Viking hb £12.99
0670882275
A contemporary slant on Aesop. This is a hilarious and fantastically quirky picture book from a renowned duo responsible for the Stinky Cheeseman And Other Stupid Tales.
7+

TALES FROM THE MABINOGION

Gwyn Thomas and Kevin Crossley-Holland
Penguin pb £6.99
0140388540

The Mabinogion is the title usually given to a collection of eleven medieval Welsh tales. This book includes four 'branches' of the Mabinogion and a glossary of Welsh names. These magical stories are complemented with illustrations which give a taste of Welsh folklore told for centuries.
7+

GREEK AND NORSE LEGENDS

Usborne pb £7.99 0746002408
An illustrated introduction to the world of Greek and Norse myths and legends. Simple plot outlines of the major stories combine with brief sketches of the main characters in an ideal reference work. The book includes a useful who's who of each mythology.
7-9

STORIES FOR CHILDREN

Oscar Wilde, illustrations PJ Lynch
Macdonald pb £7.99
0750009993

Wilde said his stories were 'not for children but for childlike people' and indeed they are subtle and melancholy in a very adult way. He drew much inspiration from Hans Andersen. This is a lavish and stunningly illustrated collection of six of Wilde's best-loved fairy tales, including The Selfish Giant and The Happy Prince.

GREEK MYTHS FOR YOUNG CHILDREN

Marcia Williams
Walker pb £4.99 074453075X
Orpheus and Eurydice, Perseus and the Gorgon's Head and six other Greek myths retold in the style of a cartoon-strip for young children. The hilarious and detailed illustrations combine perfectly with an irreverent text to provide an entertaining introduction to these stories.
6-9

FAIRY TALES BY TERRY JONES

FICTION 9-12

This is the next step on from the books in the young reader's section. Now they are reading independently, children have a vast world of books in front of them which is waiting to be devoured. In this section there are classics, prizewinners and stories to suit everyone.

Some children will already know what they demand from their stories. Others may feel apprehensive and feel overwhelmed by the choice on the bookshelves. For this reason there is a range of complexity within this section – ideal for reluctant readers and for good readers who want a break from a more challenging read, just as adults do.

There are as many different styles as there are in adult fiction; humour, science fiction, detective stories and fantasy are just some of them.

We have represented as many authors as possible. Most of them have written several books and more can be found in your bookshop. These reviews give a taste of their stories and style. Discover new authors and enjoy exploring.

THE IRON MAN

WATERSHIP DOWN
Richard Adams
Puffin pb £6.99 014064536
This classic tale tells of the determination and courage of a group of rabbits fleeing from danger in search of a new home. Facing huge odds, Hazel leads them to a new life. Beautifully written, this story is touching, breath-taking and as a parable of 20th century living, very thought-provoking.

WOOF

THE GIANT BABY
Allan Ahlberg
Puffin pb £4.99 0140363807
Alice is desperate for a baby brother but her parents are less keen. One night a giant baby is left on their doorstep and clearly has to be looked after. But it's hard to stop a huge baby becoming the centre of attention; there's the police, the council and even the local circus. How will they manage to protect him?

WOOF!
Allan Ahlberg
Puffin pb £3.50 0140319964
One night Eric is alarmed to find he has turned into a dog, and is even more puzzled to find he has changed back the next morning. Then it happens again at the swimming pool.

Why does Eric keep changing and what can he do about it?
99

NECKLACE OF RAINDROPS
Joan Aiken
Puffin pb £5.99 0140307540
A magical collection of short stories which blend dream, fairy tales and myths into fantastic stories of a girl who lives in the sky, a giant cat, an airborne apple pie and other flights of the imagination. All stories are strikingly illustrated by Jan Pienkowski.

WOLVES OF WILLOUGHBY CHASE
Joan Aiken
Red Fox pb £3.50 0099972506
A nineteenth century that never was, with James III on the throne and wolves roaming the forests, provides the perfect background for

this witty and dramatic tale peopled with marvellously Dickensian characters. Chief of these is the scheming Miss Slightcarp who has an evil plan. Blackhearts in Battersea is the compelling sequel.
99

LITTLE WOMEN
Louisa M Alcott
Puffin pb £3.99 0140366687
First published in 1868, Little Women remains compelling today. It is the story of the four March sisters, growing up in New England against the background of the American Civil War. Still both funny and moving, it also has wonderful Jo March – one of the ultimate, feisty heroines in children's books.
99

BILLY THE SQUID

BARRINGTON STOKE

This is a new publisher that specialises in books for children who find reading difficult. Maybe they are dyslexic, are learning English as a second language or just lack confidence. The books have short chapters, frequent paragraph breaks and lots of illustrations. They are written by well-known authors, Michael Morpurgo and Vivian French to name but two, and are gripping, exciting stories. Best of all they are not patronising and fill a necessary gap in the children's book market for older readers with a younger reading age.

PETER PAN
JM Barrie
Puffin pb £3.99 0140366741
...or the boy who never grew up. Written originally as a play, this is the story of the three Darling children who fly with Peter to Never Never Land, with its Indians, Pirates and Tinkerbell the fairy. A book which never fails to enchant today with its mixture of magic and adventure.
99

CARRIE'S WAR
Nina Bawden
Puffin pb £5.99 0140364560
Carrie and her brother are evacuated to Wales during the Second World War, and find it hard to settle into their new home. They soon learn, however, to take advantage of their new-found freedom, which in turn liberates the people around them.
99

THE PEPPERMINT PIG
Nina Bawden
Puffin pb £4.99 0140309446
The feisty central character of Poll brings to life this story of a family's change of circumstance at the turn of the century. Throughout a frequently difficult year, Johnnie the Peppermint pig, the best thing about their new life, grows from a tiny piglet to fat maturity.
99

HACKER
Malorie Blackman
Transworld pb £3.99
0552527513
Vicky Gibb's father is accused of stealing over a million pounds from the bank where he works. Desperate to prove his innocence, Vicky learns about what really happened as well as things about herself.

PIG-HEART BOY
Malorie Blackman
Yearling pb £3.99
0552528412

Cameron is getting more sick by the day. His heart is failing and he needs a transplant. He gets the offer of a pig's heart. The operation is experimental and risky but only Cameron can make this decision. A positive, engrossing story of relationships and fears.

Judy Blume

Judy Blume's books are consistently warm, humorous and readable and have made her a much loved and respected author in many countries. She is best known for her ability to express the complex emotions children experience as they grow up, never shying away from difficult or embarrassing issues.

BLUBBER
Judy Blume
Macmillan pb £3.50
0330263293

The class begins to tease Linda about being fat; Jill Brenner is one of the ringleaders. However, when the tables are suddenly turned, she finds things aren't so funny on the other side.

TALES OF A FOURTH GRADE NOTHING
Judy Blume
Macmillan pb £3.50
0330262114

Nine year old Peter Hatcher's life is beset by problems, the biggest of which is his younger brother Fudge – and nobody appreciates quite what Peter has to go through! The first in several stories about Peter, Fudge and Sheila.

99

Enid Blyton

Probably one of the best known children's authors, and certainly the most prolific, Blyton's books have gone in and out of fashion with adults but have never lost their popularity with children. Her stories are formulaic, comfortable and escapist reads about adult-free worlds. Especially good for reluctant readers.

THE ENCHANTED WOOD
Enid Blyton
Mammoth pb £3.99
0749708034

Jo, Bessie and Fanny discover an enchanted wood, and the faraway tree at the top which is a different land every time they visit. The first book in a series which follows the magical adventure they have with the fairy-folk of the woods.

99

THE ISLAND OF ADVENTURE
Enid Blyton
Macmillan pb £3.99
0330333631

First in a series of stories in which four children and their talking parrot inadvertently fall into an adventure by way of the statutory secret passages and deserted mines. Guaranteed to capture the imagination of most children.

99

WOOF

THE CHILDREN OF GREEN KNOWE
Lucy M Boston
Puffin pb £3.99 0140364617
When Tolly goes to live with his great-grandmother, little does he know what a wonderful time he will have, for hers is a very special house which Tolly finds he is sharing with children who lived many years ago.

Henrietta Branford

Henrietta Branford is a prolific writer of fiction for all age groups. As well as winning various prizes her books have been Waterstone's Book of the Month numerous times. Her books are pacy, sometimes challenging reads and deal with such a variety of topics that every child will find one that he or she will enjoy.

DIMANCHE DILLER
Henrietta Branford
Collins pb £2.99
0006747485
Valburga is Dimanche Diller's horrible guardian - or is she? There seem to be lots of adventures happening - are there evil plans afoot? Luckily Dimanche has her nanny to help her.

FIRE, BED AND BONE
Henrietta Branford
Walker pb £3.99 0744554855
The year is 1381. There has been plague and hardship and now the peasants are ready to fight back. The battles and adventures are told through a dog as she fights for her family and those who love her.

SPACEBABY
Henrietta Branford
Collins pb £3.99 000675175X
A talking baby from outer space? Tipperary and her dog, Hector, are surprised but they listen to what the baby has to say. Gravity is going wrong and they have three days to save the Earth. Unfortunately Silas Stoatwarden has other ideas...

THE SCHOOL AT THE CHALET
Elinor Brent-Dyer
Collins pb £3.99 0006925170
A young English woman decides to set up a school for girls in the Austrian Tyrol - a cosmopolitan environment in which many adventures take place. First published in 1926, this is the first in a long and much-loved series about the Chalet school.

THE DEMON HEADMASTER

WHISPERS IN THE GRAVEYARD
Theresa Breslin
Mammoth pb £3.50
0749723882
Solomon, a dyslexic, let down by his parents and his teachers, suddenly finds himself called upon to save a young girl from a dreadful fate. A gripping novel, which sets stark social realism against a tense psychological and supernatural drama.

,,

A LITTLE PRINCESS
Frances Hodgson Burnett
Puffin pb £3.99 0140366881
Privileged Sarah Crewe, star pupil at Miss Minchin's Academy, is reduced to servant status when her father loses his fortune - but, nevertheless, she retains her dignity, good spirits and several close friends. A fairytale like story, loved by generations of children, in which purity and courage triumph over corruption.

,,

THE SECRET GARDEN
Frances Hodgson Burnett
Puffin pb £2.99 0140366660
After the death of her parents, contrary Mary Lennox is brought from India to live in her uncle's enormous house in Yorkshire. Here she discovers a 'secret garden' and slowly learns to enjoy the world around her. A beautifully-written story which explores the emotional development of several characters.

,,

THE INCREDIBLE JOURNEY
Sheila Burnford
Hodder pb £3.99 0340626658
Follow the adventures of a labrador, a bull terrier and a Siamese cat as they travel through the wilderness to find their home. A classic story of courage and loyalty for all animal lovers, upon which the Disney film 'Homeward Bound' was based.

,,

ALICE IN WONDERLAND
Lewis Carroll
Puffin pb £4.99 0140383514
A brilliant, funny and frequently surreal child's-eye view of a nonsensical, illogical world. Alice's Adventures in Wonderland and Through the Looking Glass are undisputed classics, having given us some of the best known and best-loved characters in children's literature. Through the Looking Glass is also available from Puffin and several gift versions are in print. Look out for the lovely Macmillan editions with Tenniel's original illustrations.

,,

SOCCER AT SANDFORD
Rob Childs
Transworld pb £2.99
044086318X
A book for the football-mad reluctant reader, which follows the excitements and disappointments of the talented young footballers at Sandford Primary School during one season.

WORM SONGS
Ann Coburn
Red Fox pb £2.99 0099643111
First Frankie gatecrashes the photography club and then she takes over David, Alice and Michael's project. Together they go on a sunset shoot and the image of a mysterious woman is caught on film. They begin to investigate who she is and are caught on the edges of past and present. This is the first book in the Borderlands Sequence; you can read more in Web Weaver and Water Songs.

,,

UNDER THE HAWTHORN TREE
Marita Conlon-McKenna
O'Brien pb £3.99 0862782066
The Irish famine of the 1840s is dramatically brought to life in this epic tale. Three brave children undertake the treacherous journey to Castle Taggart to find their fabled great-aunts. A heart-rending tale of courage and strength.

WHAT KATY DID
Susan Coolidge
Puffin pb £3.50 0140366970
Written at about the same time as Little Women, and also American, this is a very different book. The story of irrepressible Katy Carr who always means to be as good as an angel but never quite manages it!

"

THE DARK IS RISING SEQUENCE
Susan Cooper
Puffin pb £11.00 0140316884
Omnibus edition of the thrilling fantasy series, which is rich in myth and Celtic legend and bristling with atmosphere. Individual titles also available.

BAGTHORPES BESIEGED
Helen Cresswell
Faber pb £4.99 0571179487
There is more mayhem in this latest book in the madcap Bagthorpe series. Mr Bagthorpe is suspected of being a terrorist and a murderer, Grandma is writing terrible memoirs and little Daisy Parker is obsessed with death. The chaos abounds. This is another hilarious read in this classic series.

THE DEMON HEADMASTER
Gillian Cross
Puffin pb £4.99 0140316434
From the first day, Dinah can tell that her new school isn't normal. Immaculate, regimented children recite facts and dates in the playground, and there's a whiff of fear in the air. What, or who, are they frightened of?

"

THE GREAT ELEPHANT CHASE
Gillian Cross
Puffin pb £4.99 0140363610
Two children travel across America, drawing on their instinct for survival and the power of their friendship, as they struggle to save their elephant from exploitation. An exhilarating adventure.

MATILDA

Morris Gleitzman

Morris Gleitzman was born in England but emigrated to Australia when he was sixteen. He has tried many things for a career but settled on writing books for children, with a bit of journalism thrown in. So why does he love doing this so much?

Author by author

I grew up in South London (best fish and chips in the world, see Misery Guts) and emigrated to Australia (second best fish and chips in the world, see Worry Warts) with my family when I was sixteen.

I didn't have the wrists for shearing sheep, so I threw into being a frozen chicken thawer, sugar mill rolling stock unhooker, fashion industry trainee, student, department store Santa, TV producer, newspaper columnist and screenwriter (not all at once).

Then in 1985 I wrote a novel for young people. Now I'm a children's author. I love it because it's one of the few jobs you can do at home in your pyjamas. It's never boring because you get out a lot in your imagination. And when a book's finished you get out a lot in real life to travel and promote it. Plus you get to eat fish and chips for research. I reckon I'm really lucky I've got weak wrists.

Some books by
Morris Gleitzman

Misery Guts
Worry Warts
Blabber Mouth
Two Weeks With The Queen
Belly Flop
Water Wings

all published by Macmillan

Roald Dahl

Roald Dahl is one of the most popular children's writers in print. His witty and, at times, disturbing prose addresses many issues that matter to children. His genius is the product of a sense of humour and an ability to understand what it is about stories that children like. His own experiences as a child, recounted in 'Boy' are to be found in his writing – being ignored or mistreated are recurrent themes. His humorous heroes and heroines always win battles against adult injustice and oppression. The books are funny and the plots fantastic; children know that Roald Dahl is on their side.

MATILDA

CHARLIE & THE CHOCOLATE FACTORY
Roald Dahl
Puffin pb £4.50 0140371540
Poverty-stricken Charlie is amazed to find he has won a trip to Willy Wonka's amazing chocolate factory, along with four horrible children. As the fantastic tour goes on the others get distracted by the magical sweets until there is just Charlie left, and then he finds out exactly what wonderful prize he has won.
"

JAMES AND THE GIANT PEACH
Roald Dahl
Puffin pb £3.99 0143042699
James lives with his awful aunts who make his life a misery. The growth of an amazing giant peach in their garden changes his life, as its inhabitants – some magical giant insects – rescue James and take him on a fantastic journey.
"

MATILDA
Roald Dahl
Puffin pb £4.50 0140327592
A little girl escapes the loneliness of her world and the unpleasantness of her family through reading books. This opens her mind to psychic powers which she uses to save her beloved class teacher and schoolmates from their bullying headmistress. A thought-provoking book about the ill treatment of children, handled in a light-hearted way.
"

THE BFG
Roald Dahl
Puffin pb £4.50 0140315977
Sophie the orphan is kidnapped by a giant and fears she will be eaten. She has, however, been taken by a big friendly giant, and together they hatch a clever plan to stop the other giants eating children ever again.

THE WITCHES
Roald Dahl
Puffin pb £4.50 0140317309
The witches of England hatch a plan to turn all the children into mice. They test the potion on the one boy who has been warned about these ghastly hags by his wise grandmother. He must then use his new mousy wits to survive and plan his revenge upon them. This book has a surprising ending, which, although unconventional, fits the story perfectly.
"

Don't forget all the other great titles …

CHARLIE & THE GREAT GLASS ELEVATOR
DANNY THE CHAMPION OF THE WORLD
ESIO TROT
GEORGE'S MARVELLOUS MEDICINE
THE TWITS

KITTENS IN THE KITCHEN
Lucy Daniels
Hodder pb £2.99 034060722X
Mandy is an animal lover and helps her parents in their veterinary surgery. When a stray cat has unwanted kittens in a neighbour's kitchen, Mandy has only a week to find homes for the lot.
The first book in the popular series Animal Ark.
99

TUDOR TERROR:THE KING IN BLOOD RED AND GOLD
Terry Deary
Dolphin pb £3.99 1858815177
Murder and intrigue on the Scottish borders in Tudor times. One of Queen Elizabeth's spies arrives at Marsden Manor and persuades Will and his grandfather to join him on a dangerous mission. As they go, grandfather tells the exciting story of his own travels into Scotland in King Henry VIII's time.

MOONFLEET
JM Falkner
Puffin pb £3.50 0140367047
This classic tale of 18th Century smugglers has all the ingredients of a good yarn - buried treasure, dark deeds, the curse of Colonel 'Blackbeard' Mohune and some deliciously horrible encounters with corpses in dark tunnels.
99

CHARLOTTE SOMETIMES
Penelope Farmer
Puffin pb £4.25 0140360840
Off to boarding school for the first time, Charlotte discovers an unexpected problem; she has slipped back to 1918 with a different personality and a new name, Clare. Time-travel is confusing and tiring. Then Clare disappears – will Charlotte be stuck in 1918 for good?
99

Anne Fine

Multi-award-winning Anne Fine writes with humour and understanding about difficult issues. Very well-written and very readable, her books have been adapted for television and the cinema.

FLOUR BABIES
Anne Fine
Puffin pb £3.99 0140361472
The flour babies are bags of flour which class 4C, much to their disgust, have to care for night and day for three weeks as part of the school science fair. Gradually, in this funny and tender story, the class become aware of the responsibilities of parenthood.
99 ☆

CHARLIE AND THE CHOCOLATE FACTORY

GOGGLE EYES
Anne Fine
Puffin pb £3.75 0140340718
The humorous and touching account of how a girl learns to accept her mother's new boyfriend.

WAR BOY
Michael Foreman
Puffin pb £3.50 0140342990
Foreman writes and illustrates his own war-time childhood memories of a Suffolk village, where his mother owned a corner shop. An informative, humorous and moving account of the war. A gift edition is also available (Pavilion, 1851453539)

HELLO? IS ANYONE THERE?
Jostein Gaarder
Dolphin pb £3.99
1858816238
Joe makes friends with a little boy from space who lands in his garden. Mika has never been to earth before and he wants to know everything. What is a telephone? What is the alphabet? As Joe tries to answer he realises what an amazing place the world is. This is a gentle thought-provoking story.

THE WEIRDSTONE OF BRISINGAMEN
Alan Garner
Collins pb £3.99 0006742939
Colin and Susan meet a wizard and creatures from the underworld, as their own lives get mixed up with the magic of ancient legends.

THE FAMILY FROM ONE END STREET
Eve Garnett
Puffin pb £3.99
0140367756
Winner of the Carnegie Medal, this book was first published in 1937 and was intended to highlight the poverty of urban children between the wars. However, it quickly established itself as an entertaining story of family life and remains timelessly enjoyable.

THE IRON MAN

Jacqueline Wilson

Jacqueline Wilson is one of Britain's most popular writers today. She writes about people, families and very real lives and is funny with it. All her books include illustrations by Nick Sharratt.

Author by author

When I was nine I solemnly declared I was going to write a novel. I'd been playing elaborate mind games ever since I was little and writing page-long stories in tiny Woolworths exercise books – but now I felt ready for the Bigtime look. I was only a child but I'd always longed for brothers and sisters, so I made up a story about a very large family. Dad worked on the buses and mum looked after the seven children. There was a boy-mad blonde teenager, a shy bookish twelve year old, a sparky ten year old desperate to be an actress, twins of nine, a timid boy of six and a ferocious curly-haired toddler.

I only managed about twelve pages and I'm afraid my prose style shows I wasn't a literary infant phenomenon, but I suppose we all have to start somewhere! If I were writing the same story now, I'd have Dad being a house-husband and Mum working on the buses – but the children are still very much the sort that I write about now.

Some books by
Jacqueline Wilson
Buried Alive
The Lottie Project
Bad Girls
The Bed And Breakfast
Star
The Story Of Tracy
Beaker
Double Act

all published by Transworld

Morris Gleitzman

Born in England but now living in Australia, Morris Gleitzman has written many excellent and compelling children's books. His stories tend to be very funny and rather off-beat, despite dealing with some serious issues, such as illness, death and disability.

BELLY FLOP
Morris Gleitzman
Macmillan pb £3.99
0330345222
Mitch has decided that he needs to become a champion diver so that people will stop hating him and his family. Luckily, he has a guardian angel called Doug who he can talk to and who will give him the help he needs.

TWO WEEKS WITH THE QUEEN
Morris Gleitzman
Macmillan pb £3.50
0330313762
Luke has cancer, and his brother Colin decides that the one person who could help is the Queen. Crazy attempts to contact her ensue, including phone calls to the Royale Fish Bar, Peckham. Complex issues approached with humour and directness.

THE DIDDAKOI
Rumer Godden
Macmillan pb £3.50
0330323970
Kizzy doesn't care that she's teased at school for being half gypsy – a 'diddakoi'. She lives in a caravan with her Gran and Old Joe the caravan horse, and everything is fine – until her Gran dies, and the world she knows and loves comes under threat.

"

Excellent Extras
1 Asterix was first published in Britain in 1969.
2 The bestselling Asterix in Britain is 'Asterix in Britain'
3 In the latest Asterix book, Asterix and Obelix All At Sea, Kirk Douglas makes an appearance as do new characters such as Absolutelyfabulos.

THE WIND IN THE WILLOWS
Kenneth Grahame
Puffin pb £2.99 0140366857
The immortal story of Mole, Ratty, Badger and Toad and their lives along the banks of the river, messing about in boats or attempting to defeat the weasels and stoats in the Wild Wood. Very much a book of its time, but one that retains pertinence

through its vivid and humorous characterisation.

"

THE WIZARD OF EARTHSEA
Ursula le Guin
Puffin pb £3.99 0140364609
After Sparrowhawk uses magic to save his village, he is sent to the school for Wizards to learn to control his power. There his boastful pride betrays him and he unwittingly releases a dark force in the world that pursues him to the ends of the earth. First in a series.

"

THE LAST VAMPIRE
Willis Hall
Red Fox pb £2.99 0099221020
Henry Hollins and his parents are on their first trip abroad, travelling around Europe. They end up at the castle Alucard which appears to be deserted - but is it? The villagers are acting very strangely too - what's going on? A hilarious tale with more in the series to enjoy as well.

"

THE ADVENTURES OF TINTIN
Hergé
Mammoth pb £4.99
Hergé combines his precise, easy and immediately recognisable visual style with good-natured, adventure-packed stories in over 20

different books. From the wry linguistic humour of 'The Broken Ear' to the hard-nosed industrial espionage of 'The Calculus Affair' and the heart-warming pathos of 'Tintin in Tibet'. With a cast of wonderfully rounded and instantly recognisable characters, there are adventures for all sorts of moods and all sorts of readers.

"

BEAVER TOWERS
Nigel Hinton
Puffin pb £3.25 0140370609
Philip is flown by magic to an island where the beavers, Mr Edgar and Baby B, and their friends are the last resistance against the evil witch, Oyin. It seems that Philip is to be their unlikely saviour!

"

I AM DAVID
Anne Holm
Mammoth pb £3.99 0749701366
When David escapes from prison camp and 'them', he faces a long and difficult journey, the unlearning of fear, and the learning of hope.

Anthony Horowitz

Anthony Horowitz tries to write something every day and he says that he never writes about anything or anywhere that he hasn't seen. His books are often comedy thrillers and spoofs and are less to do with issues and more to do with good escapist storytelling.

GROOSHAM GRANGE
Anthony Horowitz
Walker pb £3.99 0744547121
What kind of school collects its new pupils in a hearse, and makes them sign in blood? Packed full of quick fire jokes that make you laugh and groan and a cast of weird characters straight out of a spoof horror film.

THE LAST GOLD DIGGERS
Harry Horse
Puffin pb £3.99 0140376763
The hilarious expedition of Grandfather and Roo, the dog with her own strong opinions, to Australia to find long-lost Uncle Vincent. Their crazy adventures are told in Grandfather's letters home and through his diaries. Roo is too busy rabbiting to add anything personally.

Carol Hughes

Carol Hughes' stories are what used to be called 'good yarns'. They are exciting, escapist adventures with a comforting feel which absorb any reader.

JACK BLACK AND THE SHIP OF THIEVES
Carol Hughes
Blooomsbury £4.99 0747534861
Giant airships, volcanic islands, warships without crews, heroic pirates and treacherous friends all feature in this exhilarating tale. Reminiscent of Victorian adventure stories but with a distinctly modern edge, this is a gripping read.

THE IRON MAN

TOOTS AND THE UPSIDE DOWN HOUSE
Carol Hughes
Bloomsbury pb £3.99
074752663X

One minute Toots is sat on the floor. The next she is tiny and on the ceiling with a plump fairy. On a mission to save her teddy bear there are lots of adventures with goblins and sprites. How will she manage to get back to her father? Toots is upside down in the garden in her next adventures.

THE IRON MAN
Ted Hughes
Faber pb £3.99 0571141498
The huge Iron Man roams the land, and feeds on old cars and machinery. Hailed as a modern classic, this

tale contains some startling imagery, which makes it a rich and rewarding book.
"

THE SECRET OF PLATFORM 13
Eva Ibbotson
Macmillan pb £3.50
0330337483
Under platform 13 at King's Cross Station, there is a gump. It is open for 9 days, every 9 years and the last time it was open, a royal prince was stolen. Now a hand-picked team must rescue him, even though he's not very cooperative.

LITTLE HOUSE IN THE BIG WOODS
Laura Ingalls Wilder
Mammoth pb £3.99
0749709316
First in a series of books about a pioneering childhood spent travelling

across America 120 years ago, through land shared with bears and wolves. Beautifully written, and all the more captivating because it is true.

Excellent Extras
Brian Jacques likes to write his books in his garden between May and September. If it rains he has an enormous umbrella to keep him dry.

REDWALL SERIES
Brian Jacques
Red Fox pb £4.50 each
The Redwall books have become one of the best-selling series of the last 10 years. The first one, 'Redwall' was nominated for the Carnegie award and with eight currently in the series there is plenty to keep even the most avid reader going! Populated with warrior otters, brave mousemaids and cut-throat weasels, this is an exciting and unmissable fantasy series.

THE LAST GOLD DIGGERS

Paula Danziger

The American Paula Danziger was a teacher, has a home on both sides of the Atlantic and has appeared many times on British T.V. This is the explanation of why one of her characters, Amber Brown, is who she is.

Author by author

When I was little, my favourite book was 'The Little Engine That Could'. Sometimes I think that I and my character, Amber Brown, are like that engine. Sometimes we 'chug along' and sometimes we move quickly to bring important things to kids (okay…so the train brought toys and candy…but Amber and I bring messages about the ability to look at and live through not only good but difficult times and know that there are ways to handle situations. And we also show that sometimes a sense of perspective and a sense of humour go a long way).

Where does Amber Brown come from? She comes from my imagination, my observations and my experiences. She also comes from America but she has a lot of English influences.

In the beginning, I based her on my niece who has a very different life to Amber. But they both have guts, intelligence and an original way of looking at the world.

I've had British friends help me do the research for the Amber books. We've baked Amber brownies together (the tunafish brownies were the worse!) …we've nail polish and decorating parties and I've visited classrooms to get ideas.

Speaking of ideas…..what do you think the next Amber book should be called?

Some books by Paula Danziger
Amber Brown Goes Forth
Amber Brown Is Not A Crayon
Amber Brown Wants Extra Credit
Forever Amber Brown

all published by Mammoth

FINN FAMILY MOOMINTROLL

Tove Jansson
Puffin pb £4.99 014030150X
When Moomintroll finds a tall, black hat, he has no idea that it belongs to a hobgoblin - but everyone notices when peculiar things begin to happen. These magical stories about the Moomins (small, fat, endearing beasts), manage to combine strange, almost surreal elements with comfortingly familiar domestic detail.

THE GIZMO

Paul Jennings
Puffin pb £3.99 0140370900
Stephen steals a gizmo and strange things begin to happen. What's worse is that he does not seem to be able to get rid of it. It's paying him back for taking it.

UNREAL!

Paul Jennings
Puffin pb £3.50 0140370994
A collection of characteristically quirky stories from a master of the bizarre. Bones that want to be reunited, ghosts that play 'we shall not be moved' on the clarinet and saxophone - these strange tales will delight children with active imaginations.

99

Excellent Extras

Robin Jarvis also illustrates all his own books. He used to make 3D models for Channel 4 and he still makes models of some of his characters.

Robin Jarvis

The thoroughly gripping, fast-paced books of Robin Jarvis contain themes of good versus evil. They involve sorcery, mystery, terror and are full of strange beasts, witches and even a foul-mouthed teddy bear who talks with an American drawl. The human, animal and magical worlds entwine in these series.

Deptford Histories

ALCHEMIST'S CAT
OAKEN THRONE
THOMAS

Deptford Mice

DARK PORTAL
CRYSTAL PRISON
FINAL RECKONING

Whitby Series

WHITBY WITCHES
A WARLOCK IN WHITBY
THE WHITBY CHILD

All Macdonald Young Books
£5.99

Tales from the Wyrd Musem

THE WOVEN PATH
0006750125 Raven's Knot
Fatal Strand (April 1999)
Collins pb £5.99

THE PHANTOM TOLLBOOTH

Norman Juster
Collins pb £3.99 0006725880
Milo was bored, very bored - until he met a ticking watchdog called 'Tock', the smallest giant in the world, a mathamagician and many, many other puzzling characters. Milo has no time to be bored and nor will any reader picking up this intriguing book.

EMIL & THE DETECTIVES

Eric Kastner
Red Fox pb £3.50 0099293617
After being robbed, Emil is let down by unbelieving authorities. With a group of youngsters he turns private eye and seeks justice. A classic detective story.

99

OUT OF THE HITLER TIME

Judith Kerr
Collins pb £9.99 000675077X
This is the omnibus edition of the trilogy which is based on the author's own family during World War Two. As a child Anna escapes from the Nazis, as an adolescent she is

state-less in London and as a woman marries happily. But maybe she can never escape her past.

STIG OF THE DUMP
Clive King
Puffin pb £4.50 0140364501
Stig of the Dump is full of secrets. How do you tell your Grandma that you are playing with a stone-age boy? How do you believe it yourself when you return a year later for another 'boring' holiday with Gran? Though fantastical, this book is really about the friendship of children in a sometimes dangerous world.
"

A MOUSE CALLED WOLF
Dick King-Smith
Corgi Yearling pb £3.99
0440863716
Wolfgang Amadeus is a very long name for a little mouse. But it's a perfect name because Wolf has a very unusual talent among mice-he has a beautiful singing voice. It also means that he can help a friend in need.

THE SHEEP PIG
Dick King-Smith
Puffin pb £3.99 0140318399
Dick King-Smith has the knack of turning mundane creatures into wonderful heroes. Who would believe

a pig could talk ...but that would be telling. This is an exciting and touching story about an unlikely hero.

THE QUEEN'S NOSE
Dick King-Smith
Puffin pb £3.99 0140318380
The combination of richly observed reality, from a child's point of view, and fantastical magic makes 'The Queen's Nose' enchanting. The reality starts in an old smelly chicken hut at the bottom of a wet suburban garden. The magic starts when this dull scene is transformed by our heroine's imagination into a pagoda in an Indian jungle.
"

THE JUNGLE BOOK
Rudyard Kipling
Puffin pb £2.99 0140366865
The well-known and well-loved story of Mowgli, the man-cub brought up by wolves and taught the law of the jungle. The book also contains other stories from India, including Rikki-tikki-tavi the Mongoose, and Toomai of the Elephants.
"

THE SHEEP PIG

HIDING OUT
Elizabeth Laird
Mammoth pb £4.50
0749716649

What would you do if you were left behind with no food, no money, no home and nobody? Peter has to find the answers to these questions the hard way. A very credible and well written story.

99

THE LION, THE WITCH AND THE WARDROBE
C.S. Lewis
Collins pb £3.99 0006716636

The second book to be written in the magical Narnia series. The four Pevensey children, stumble through the back of a wardrobe into the fantastical world of Narnia, which is in the grip of an evil white witch. Essential reading for imaginative children.

PIPPI LONGSTOCKING
Astrid Lindgren
Puffin pb £4.99 0140308946

Pippi, a remarkably strong young girl, lives a life without adults, that most can only dream of. With no one to answer to, she has a series of adventures that leaves the reader and her more conventional neighbours amazed and amused.

99

THE STORY OF DOCTOR DOLITTLE
Hugh Lofting
Red Fox pb £3.99 0099854600

Doctor Dolittle prefers the company of animals to that of humans, and does indeed talk to them. In the first story of the series the Doctor travels to Africa, and has a succession of extraordinary adventures.

99

BACK HOME
Michelle Magorian
Puffin pb £4.99 0140319077

Austere, post-war Britain comes as a terrible shock to Rusty after five years as an evacuee in affluent America with a caring, easy-going foster family. Rusty needs every ounce of her indomitable spirit to cope with a stern and distant family and a new school deeply hostile to her American accent and ways. A deeply satisfying book with an outspoken heroine who won't ever learn to do the 'done thing'.

GOODNIGHT MR TOM
Michelle Magorian
Puffin pb £4.99 0140315411

When Willie Beech, an unloved and lonely evacuee, is billeted with Tom Oakley, a stubborn and equally solitary old man, they begin tentatively to form a bond of love both unexpected and unsought. When

GOODNIGHT MR TOM

Willie is recalled to London and disappears, Tom is finally galvanised into action. A harrowing and powerful book.

"

THE HAUNTING
Margaret Mahy
Puffin pb £4.99 0140363254
Barney is frightened. He's being haunted, and the voice and the footsteps are getting closer. As much about a family as the supernatural, the eerie and claustrophobic atmosphere is balanced with great warmth and humour.

"

WALKABOUT
James Vance Marshall
Puffin pb £3.50 0140312927
Sole survivors of a plane crash in the Australian desert, Mary and her younger brother Peter will certainly die, but then an Aboriginal boy finds them and teaches them to survive in the outback, giving them the spirit to survive and go on even after his own death.

THE BABYSITTERS CLUB
Ann M Martin
Scholastic pb £2.50
Stories from the members of the Babysitters Club, told in their own voices, about the fun, the trials and the tribulations of pre-teenage life and serious babysitting.

THE BOX OF DELIGHTS
John Masefield
Mammoth pb £3.99
0749712864
When Kay meets a mysterious Punch and Judy man, he becomes involved in a strange and thrilling adventure. Evil Abner Brown and his dangerous wolves will do anything to obtain the magical box, and only Kay can stop them. A brilliantly exciting story unfolds …

"

THE EXILES
Hilary McKay
Collins pb £3.99 0006746438
Big Grandma thinks her eccentric and headstrong grand-daughters do too much reading and not enough living, so when they are sent, under duress, to stay with her, a ban on reading produces some extraordinary results.

WINNIE THE POOH
AA Milne
Mammoth pb £4.99
0749707100
All-time classic favourites, these stories of Christopher Robin and his bear, not to mention Piglet, Eeyore, Owl and Rabbit, are an intrinsic part of most childhoods. Funny and quirky, they are excellent for reading aloud

to younger children. More gentle adventures in 'The House at Pooh Corner'.

Gift editions available.

"

ANNE OF GREEN GABLES
LM Montgomery
Puffin pb £3.99 0140367411
The first, and best-known of the ten books about vivacious Anne Shirley, a red-haired orphan who invades the lives of a quiet Canadian farming family. Drawn from the author's real life experiences with her grandparents on Prince Edward Island at the end of the last century.

"

TOOTH AND CLAW
Stephen Moore
Hodder pb £3.99
0340704543
Reminiscent of Mrs Frisby and the Rats of NIMH, this is the story of the cats and dogs who are left behind in an evacuated town. This is an exciting and gritty struggle for survival.

Michael Morpurgo

Michael Morpurgo's books are compelling and highly emotive. Dropped into his magical worlds, a reader is rewarded with gripping and unusual tales.

THE BUTTERFLY LION
Michael Morpurgo
Collins pb £3.99 0006751032
This is a unique and immensely touching story. Bertie rescues a white lion cub and takes it home. Although they are separated when Bertie goes to school he swears that they will see each other again.The butterfly lion himself ensures that their friendship will not be forgotten.
99

THE WRECK OF THE ZANZIBAR
Michael Morpurgo
Mammoth pb £2.99
0749726202
In 1907 Laura decides to keep a diary. In 1995 her great nephew reads it and relives her experiences. A beautiful, but tragic tale of poverty and hope.
99

WHY THE WHALES CAME
Michael Morpurgo
Mammoth pb £3.50
074970537X
When a whale is beached, Gracie and Daniel think it deserves to live. The one person to share their view is the Birdman. Their joint battle to save the whale results in the children finding out more about the mysterious Birdman.

THE RAILWAY CHILDREN
E Nesbit
Puffin pb £2.50 0140366717
Roberta, Peter and Phyllis find their lives turned upside-down when their father has to go away unexpectedly. Leaving their London home, they move away to a small house near a railway line, which is to have a significant influence on them. A touching story, which has been loved for nearly 100 years.
99

AQUILA
Andrew Norriss
Puffin pb £3.99 0140383654
Tom and Geoff find what seems to be a spaceship which has been buried for seventeen hundred years. Exciting adventures begin; not least the best way to fly it home. Unfortunately, as they try to find out more about it, suspicious teachers begin to investigate them.
99

THE BORROWERS
Mary Norton
Puffin pb £5.99 014036451X
Pod, Homily, and Arietty are borrowers – a race of tiny people who borrow everything they need from 'Human Beans', who don't even know they exist. Then Arietty changes everything by making friends with the boy

upstairs. A story full of wit, fun and imagination – and as good an explanation as any for what happens to all those safety pins that 'just disappear'.
99

MRS FRISBY AND THE RATS OF NIMH
Robert C O'Brien
Puffin pb £4.99 0141307257
It is time for the family of mice to move to their winter home, but poor Timothy is too ill to be moved. Time is running out for Mrs Frisby and she is grateful for any help she can get. An easy to read, and funny adventure story.
99

Francine Pascal

The tremendously popular Sweet Valley Series now follows the identical Wakefield twins from the age of 7, in 'Sweet Valley Kids', right through to college years in 'Sweet Valley University'. Compulsive, easy to read, and featuring issues relevant to the age group.

BEST FRIENDS
Francine Pascal
Transworld pb £2.99
0553173758
The first book in the 'Sweet Valley Twins' series.

Elizabeth and Jessica may appear identical, but they view the world very differently. Elizabeth wants to start a newspaper, whilst Jessica is more interested in being popular.

TOM'S MIDNIGHT GARDEN
Philippa Pearce
Puffin pb £5.99 0140364544
Philippa Pearce has a reputation for crafting beautiful stories into modern classics, and this book is quite outstanding. Staying with his aunt and uncle isn't what Tom had planned for his summer holidays, but there are some surprises in store for Tom when he hears the old clock strike 13. A lovely and memorable story with a moving conclusion.

99

JOHNNY AND THE DEAD
Terry Pratchett
Corgi pb £3.99 0552527408
It's very strange but Johnny Maxwell can speak to the dead. He's got bad news for them as well; the council are selling the cemetery as a building site. But it's Halloween and together they are going to stop this happening. A fantasy story told with a wicked sense of humour.

99

ARCTIC ADVENTURE
Willard Price
Red Fox Pb £3.50 0099183218
In freezing temperatures, and with dwindling food supplies, wild animals are not all that the boys have to contend with… This is part of a popular adventure series, in which Hal and Roger travel the world to collect wild animals for their father's zoo.

Philip Pullman

Philip Pullman's stories are involving reads. With a variety of plots and mood, they often have a fantasy feel and at the same time relate to issues which concern children today.

THE FIREWORK-MAKER'S DAUGHTER
Philip Pullman
Corgi Yearling pb £3.99 0440863317
Lila wants to be a Firework-Maker but she needs to make a dangerous journey to see the Fire-Fiend. This is a gripping adventure told in a mythological way.

99

CLOCKWORK
Philip Pullman
Corgi Yearling pb £3.99 0440863430
Stories within stories. Tormented clock-makers, deadly knights and mechanical princes. Characters and events are driven along and they merge together in an unstoppable, sometimes macabre, way.

99

THE FIREWORK-MAKER'S DAUGHTER

Philip Ridley

Philip Ridley's fiction explodes onto the page with great stories and amazing characters. Lively stories combine with an awareness of what children want to read in their books. They often have a modern fairy-tale feel.

Excellent Extras

Easy ways to ignore Philip Ridley:
1 Blindfold yourself as you enter an art gallery
2 Walk swiftly past the cinema (eyes fixed to the pavement)
3 Remove the power from all radios
4 Bypass the R shelf in bookshops – he's sure to be there!

SWALLOWS AND AMAZONS
Arthur Ransome
Red Fox pb £3.99 009996290X
A wonderful escapist story of childhood adventure set in the Lake District. John, Susan, Titty and Roger spend the summer camping on Wild Cat Island. When the local Amazon pirates challenge the town children to prove their seamanship, the stakes are high. This is the first in a series of sailing adventures. These famous books are also available as beautiful gift edition hardbacks.
99

THE INDIAN TRILOGY
Lynne Reid Banks
Collins pb £5.99 0006749526
The Indian in the Cupboard, Return of the Indian and The Secret of the Indian are in this omnibus. When Omri is given an old plastic Indian and an old bathroom cupboard for his birthday, it seems natural to keep them together. He has no idea that he will become responsible for the small but demanding and very real Indian. The other adventures are just as exciting.

KRINDLEKRAX
Philip Ridley
Red Fox pb £2.99 0099979209
Skinny, knock-kneed Ruskin wants to be the hero in the school play – but so does the school bully. Things don't look good until the discovery of a monster in the sewers, and Ruskin proves himself a hero after all.
99

J.K. Rowling

J.K. Rowling has had unprecedented success with the 'Harry Potter phenomenon', as it has now become. The first book 'Harry Potter And The Philosopher's Stone' won awards and raced into the best-sellers lists swiftly followed by the second 'Harry Potter and the Chamber of Secrets'. Harry's magical world of wizardry should not and will not be ignored and will continue to be added to for years to come.
She lives in Edinburgh with her young daughter.

Author by author

I have wanted to be a writer since I was five, and inflicted my earliest efforts on my younger sister. There were literally boxes full of stories and unfinished novels in my attic, most of which I must remember to burn before anyone reads them. The idea for the Harry Potter series came to me on a train in 1990 when I found myself stuck without a pen and paper (ironically I usually carry them everywhere). By the time I got off at King's Cross my brain was teeming with the characters who inhabit Hogwarts School of Witchcraft and Wizardry. The question I'm most often asked is 'where do your ideas come from?' I still haven't answered it to my satisfaction. I have no idea where ideas come from, if I knew I'd go and live there.

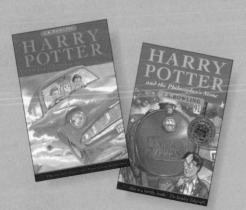

Harry Potter And The Philosopher's Stone

Harry Potter And The Chamber Of Secrets

Harry Potter And The Prisoner Of Azakaban

(July 1999)
all published by Bloomsbury

METEORITE SPOON
Philip Ridley
Puffin pb £3.99 0140368906
After their parents have a cataclysmic row, Filly and Fergal discover the land of Honeymoonia, with the aid of a magic spoon. There they meet a couple just like their parents – but the two never have a cross word.

ZINDER-ZUNDER
Philip Ridley
Puffin pb £3.99
0140385088
Max wants his Mum to notice his amazing tap-dancing and the Zinder-Zunder might just be able to help.

JOHNNY CASANOVA
Jamie Rix
Walker pb £3.99
0744547660
Johnny Worms thinks he is irresistible to women! So it shouldn't take much to convince Alison Mallinson to go out with him should it? Things don't quite go to plan in this funny story.
99

HOW TO EAT FRIED WORMS
Thomas Rockwell
Orchard pb £3.99
1852137223
Billy needs to eat 15 worms in 15 days to win fifty dollars in the bet. But when his friends find out that he might rise to this disgusting challenge they will stop at nothing to put him off. This is a really funny story.

HARRY POTTER AND THE PHILOSOPHER'S STONE
J.K Rowling
Bloomsbury pb £4.99
0747532745
Harry knows that he has a habit of making extraordinary things happen but he doesn't know how he does it. Until that is he gets to go to Hogwarts to learn wizardry and to fight the greatest evil powers. This is an exciting, thrilling, magical read. Thankfully there are more adventures to read in the sequel!

Also available
HARRY POTTER AND THE CHAMBER OF SECRETS

THE SILVER SWORD
Ian Serraillier
Puffin pb £4.50 0140364528
Based on a true story, this wonderful book tells of the struggle of four children trying to keep alive during the Nazi occupation of Poland, and of their search for their parents after the war ends. A compulsive read.
99

BLACK BEAUTY
Anna Sewell
Puffin pb £2.50 0140366849
Perhaps best known and best-loved of all animal stories, Black Beauty was originally written to highlight the cruel way horses were treated last century. A dramatic story of misfortune and eventual happiness which still appeals to the tender-hearted today.
99

METEORITE SPOON

MAN HUNT
Malaika Rose Stanley
Orchard pb £3.99 1860392326
Max is so outnumbered by
women at home that he
decides it is time to find a
man for Mum to even things
out. But it can't be just
anyone and finding the
perfect candidate leads to
very funny consequences.

101 DALMATIANS
Dodie Smith
Mammoth pb £3.99
0749702044
Dogs of every kind, from far
and wide, help Pongo and
Missis rescue their puppies
from the clutches of Cruella
de Vil. An animal adventure
that's hard to beat. Ladybird
publish versions of the Disney
movie for younger children.
99

HEIDI
Johanna Spyri
Puffin pb £2.99 0140366792
Heidi, a 5 year old orphan,
learns to love life in the Alps
with her grandfather. Both
are heartbroken when she
is sent to live in Frankfurt
with another family but she
eventually learns to love them
both. A lovely story full of
wonderful characters. Also
available in hardback.
99

Russell Stannard

Described by the Times
Educational Supplement as
'a breath of scientific fresh
air', Stannard combines
being professor of physics
at the Open University with
writing novels designed to
make science and other
'big' issues accessible and
entertaining to children.

THE TIME & SPACE OF UNCLE ALBERT
Russell Stannard
Faber pb £4.50
0571142826
Uncle Albert and his niece
Gedanken explore the
peculiarities of time and
space by means of an
imaginary space ship. Science
made simple and fun!
99

BLACK HOLES & UNCLE ALBERT
Russell Stannard
Faber pb £4.50
0571144535

UNCLE ALBERT AND THE QUANTUM QUEST
Russell Stannard
Faber pb £4.50
0571173446

TREASURE ISLAND
RL Stevenson
Puffin pb £2.99 0140366725
High seas, tall ships, pirates
and hidden treasure,
memorable characters like
Blind Pew and Long John
Silver. Cabin boy Jack
Hawkins survives all and
wins out. A classic tale which
still excites today. Available
in many other versions
from Ladybird to hardback
gift editions.
99

THE MIDNIGHT HAND
Paul Stewart
Corgi Yearling pb £3.99
0440863481
There is a feeling of fear
in Tom's new school. At
midnight he is wakend
by a severed skeleton hand
stroking his face. What does
the hand want and could
it just be leading Tom
towards danger? This is a
bloodcurdling and scary story
which will send shivers down
your spine.

WELCOME TO THE DEAD HOUSE
RL Stine
Scholastic pb £3.50 0590553089
Imagine having to move
to a huge creepy house in
a dark gloomy town –
then finding you're not
alone. First book in the
phenomenally popular and
readable 'Goosebumps' series.
99

BALLET SHOES
Noel Streatfield
Puffin pb £5.99 0140364595
Warm and involving story
of three very different girls,
adopted at birth by an
eccentric and largely absent
professor. Definitely not just
for ballet fanatics – the
experiences of the Fossils at
the Academy of Dance and
their determination to make
a mark on the world will
delight many readers.
99

THE EAGLE OF THE NINTH
Rosemary Sutcliff
Puffin pb £5.99 0140364579
A soldier sets off on a
dangerous journey, north
of Hadrian's wall, to
discover the truth about
the disappearance of an
entire Roman Legion. Can
he solve the mystery and
find the Eagle, symbol of
the legion's honour?
99

ROOM 13
Robert Swindells
Transworld pb £2.99
0440862272
Vampires and other spooky
creatures abound in this
frightening tale of Fliss's
school trip to Whitby.
Unputdownable!
99

HARRY AND THE WRINKLIES
Alan Temperley
Scholastic pb £4.99
0590113496
Harry's rich parents leave
him with the horrible
housekeeper for most of
the year but his life changes
completely when he goes to
stay with his active and
bizarre elderly aunts.

A CHILD'S CHRISTMAS IN WALES
Dylan Thomas, illustrated by Edward Ardizzone
Puffin pb £3.50 0140377239
The story of Thomas'
childhood Christmas with
all the excitement and magic
is brought to life with these
pictures. It is a modern
classic.
99

THE RUNAWAYS
Ruth Thomas
Red Fox pb £3.50 0099596601
Misfits at school and not very
happy at home, Julia and
Nathan happen to stumble
upon a large sum of money
and are forced to run away
with it. So begins an
adventure that has incredible
highs and lows and leaves

them both very different
people. A compelling and
involving story.

SWITCHERS
Kate Thompson
Red Fox pb £3.99 0099256126
Kevin knows that Tess is a
switcher because he is one
himself. They can turn into
any animal whenever they
want to. He needs her help
because strange Krools are
freezing the earth and
only they can stop the ice
spreading. The story is
magical, chilling and tense.

MARY POPPINS
PL Travers
Collins pb £5.99 0006747876
The first book about Mary
Poppins, the magical and
mischievous nanny with
a veneer of respectability.
She changes the lives of Jane
and Michael Banks forever
by whisking them off to
fantastic worlds.
99

BEYOND THE BEANSTALK
Kaye Umansky
Hodder pb £3.99
0340673060
Whatever happened to Jack
after he came down the

beanstalk? Well the money has gone and his mother is far from happy. When Mother Skinnard gives Jack more beans he cannot resist going back up to the land of giants to try his luck again.

PONGWIFFY
Kaye Umansky
Puffin pb £3.99 0140342214
The funny story about a smelly witch and her quest to outshine other witches. A very readable book with a brilliant collection of characters.
"

A TRAVELLER IN TIME
Alison Uttley
Puffin pb £3.99 0140309314
While staying with her Great Aunt in her old, atmospheric farmhouse, Penelope finds herself slipping back in time to the politically volatile Elizabethan age. As she becomes more involved with the Babington family, and the doomed plan to save Mary, Queen of Scots, the sense of tragedy increases, for she holds the awful knowledge of what will happen.

Sylvia Waugh

Sylvia Waugh was a keen storyteller and poet when she was a little girl – she and her sister used to 'fly' to imaginary lands. Her imagination is in full flow in her Mennyms series.

THE MENNYMS
Sylvia Waugh
Red Fox pb £2.99 0099301679
The strange tale of the Mennym family, who try so hard to be ordinary. Their quiet lives are threatened by a letter that heralds a visit from abroad – and if Albert Pond sets eyes upon them, he'll know they're not like other folk at all.

THE MACHINE GUNNERS
Robert Westall
Macmillan pb £3.99
033033428X
Chas McGill collects war souvenirs; so when a German plane crashes with the machine gun still intact, he is determined to have it. But in such violent times, he and his friends cannot remain content with being onlookers and collectors – they want a piece of the action.
"

CHARLOTTE'S WEB
EB White
Puffin pb £4.99 1040301852
The funny, tender story of a pig called Wilbur and his friend Charlotte's clever campaign to save him from the inevitable fate of a plump pig.

THE SWORD IN THE STONE
TH White
Collins pb £5.99 0006742009
A magical story set in an England before Arthur becomes King. Teeming with magicians, giants, knights and witches, it is a delight to read.

TARKA THE OTTER
Henry Williamson
Puffin pb £5.99 0140366210
An atmospheric, richly detailed story of an otter and her cubs and their daily struggle for survival. Ideal reading for all lovers of animals and the countryside.
"

CASTLE OF INSIDE OUT
David Henry Wilson
Macmillan pb £3.99
0330345168
A series of stories featuring young Jeremy James who, amongst other things, attempts to get rich, drive a car and understand the logic behind a christening. An entertaining child's-eye view of an often nonsensical adult world.

BAD GIRLS

Jacqueline Wilson

Jacqueline Wilson writes funny, socially aware stories which do not shy away from the problems and issues which face children at school and at home. They are fantastic, refreshing reads.

BAD GIRLS
Jacqueline Wilson
Corgi Yearling pb £3.99
0440863562
Mandy has always been picked on at school but

everything changes when she makes friends with the brave and adventurous Tanya. Mum thinks Tanya is a bad influence on Mandy and Mandy needs to work out if she is getting out of trouble or falling deeper into it.
99

THE LOTTIE PROJECT
Jacqueline Wilson
Corgi Yearling pb £3.99
044086366X
Charlie lives with her Mum and has to do a project on the Victorians. But there

are so many distractions: nerdy Jamie, money and her Mum and her friends. But was life so different in Victorian times?
99

THE BED & BREAKFAST STAR
Jacqueline Wilson
Transworld pb £2.99
0440863244
Forced to move into a run-down bed and breakfast hotel with her family, Elsa keeps her spirits up with an endless stream of jokes. Although she frequently tries the patience of her adult companions, the true value of this engaging heroine finally shines through.
99

Anthologies

Excellent Extras
Quentin Blake never had formal art training but he had his first cartoon published in 'PUNCH' magazine when he was only 16!

THE PUFFIN BOOK OF NONSENSE STORIES
ed Quentin Blake
Puffin pb £5.99 0140382135
Lewis Carroll, Edward Lear and Jane Austen provide absurd stories for this collection of nonsensical madness! Blake has added his own crazy illustrations.

INCREDIBLY CREEPY STORIES

ed Tony Bradman
Corgi pb £3.99 0552528374
Malorie Blackman, Paul Stewart and Jan Mark are among the authors in this book of ghosts and strange happenings which send shivers down your spine.

FANTASTIC STORIES

Terry Jones, illustrated by Michael Foreman
Puffin pb £4.99 0140362797
21 strange, thrilling, funny and amazing tales. There's a ship of fools, a mermaid who pitied a sailor and all kinds of animals. Not quite a collection of modern fairy tales but many of these stories are written in that style.

STORY LIBRARY: TRUE-LIFE STORIES

ed Anthony Masters
Kingfisher pb £5.99
0753402084
A selection of stories which show the key moments in the lives of 23 heroic people in recent history. They include Nelson Mandela, Marie Curie and Martin Luther King.

GHOSTLY HAUNTS

ed Michael Morpurgo
Collins pb £4.99 0006751164
Ten different authors have written new ghostly stories for this collection. The tales are made more eerie by the fact that they are based in real places and could maybe even

be true. These atmospheric stories stay with you long after the book is closed.

THE PUFFIN TREASURY OF CLASSICS

Puffin hb £19.99 0670874523
This is a beautiful gift edition of stories and verse. It includes selections from Robinson Crusoe, Pinocchio and poetry by Lewis Carroll and Rudyard Kipling. The rich variety of illustrations makes this a really inviting book.

STORY LIBRARY: FUNNY STORIES

ed Michael Rosen
Kingfisher pb £5.99
0862728010
A favourite volume from an excellent series - typically it mixes well known children's authors like Roald Dahl and Terry Jones, with tasters from James Thurber and Italo Calvino. Other titles include School Stories, Science Fiction Stories and Adventure Stories.

THE HUTCHINSON TREASURY OF CHILDREN'S LITERATURE

ed Alison Sage
Hutchinson hb £19.95
0091761441
The essential family collection of classics old and new, from Mother Goose and Quentin Blake to

Brian Jacques and Kenneth Grahame. Lavishly illustrated, often from the original texts, this will be an inviting first taste or a reminder of old favourites.

A SACKFUL OF STORIES FOR EIGHT YEAR OLDS

ed Pat Thomson
Transworld pb £2.99
0552527297
Funny and imaginative stories from favourite authors including Ted Hughes, Penelope Lively and Russell Hoban. Ideal to read aloud too. Stories from 5 through to 9 years are also available.

STORY OF THE YEAR

Scholastic
Each year The Independent runs a competition to find fresh new writers for children. The winners are published in the Story of the Year anthologies. Children are involved in the judging of the stories and the books are always popular.

BEAVER TOWERS

Philip Pullman

Philip Pullman has been lots of amazing places from Australia to South Africa (His father was in the Royal Air Force). He now lives in Oxford with his family, writes in a shed at the bottom of the garden and loves buying dictionaries. Now find out where he gets his fantastic ideas from.

Some titles by Philip Pullman

His Dark Materials I:
Northern Lights

His Dark Materials II:
Subtle Knife

The Broken Bridge

The Butterfly Tattoo

The Firework-Makers
Daughter

Clockwork

Thunderbolts Waxwork

published by Scholastic,
Transworld and Macmillan

Author by author

The most frequently asked question I get is:

"Where do you get your ideas from?"

And my most frequent answer is:

"Well, I used to go to the local Idea Centre. It's on the ring road, near Do-It-All and Sainsbury's. I spent a lot of time there looking at short story ideas and TV Series Ideas and taking Novel Ideas off the shelf to see how heavy they were, and wondering how many I could afford.

"Anyway, after several years of buying my ideas from them, I don't go there any more. I get Free Range Organic ideas now, delivered in a box every fortnight. They're more expensive but you know they're healthy, with no pesticides and so forth. And they're much better for you."

But here's the real truth:

Ideas come free all the time. The trick is to catch them before they vanish.

An even better trick is to try to do without them altogether, and just write. Only the best writers can do that. But I keep trying.

POETRY

Lullabies and Nursery Rhymes are among the first poems which children learn and are great favourites. But the enthusiasm for rhythmic text seems to wane as children get older. This is often because they think it is boring and not relevant. It is something you learn at school. Poetry as a whole has had a resurgence of popularity in recent years. This has been helped by media attention on "The Nation's Favourite Poem" choices and the annual National Poetry Day. The National Curriculum centres on the importance of poetry and, with help from teachers, the subject is becoming fun again.

This selection offers the best in anthologies for everyone to dip into and to discover poems and poets they enjoy. We have chosen beautifully illustrated picture books which set the scene and spark imagination. There are classic poems, which are reassuringly familiar, and collections of poetry on football, teacher's secrets and lots of crazy nonsense.

The poems are funny and thought provoking. Read on and see just how great poetry can be (a suggested reading age is stated).

THE PUFFIN BOOK OF UTTERLY BRILLIANT POETRY

A CARIBBEAN DOZEN
**ed John Agard and
Grace Nichols**
Walker pb £8.99 074455201X
An uplifting collection of
13 poets from the Caribbean.
Children will love the rich
rhythms of the verse and
enjoy the encounters with
exotic animals such as pum
na-na frogs and the zobo
bird, with steel bands and
with tropical fruits, with a
world in which, "English
nursery rhymes and fairy tales
mingle with the tricky doings
of Anancy Spiderman".
6+

HEARD IT IN THE PLAYGROUND
Allan Ahlberg
Puffin pb £3.99 0140328246
This sequel to 'Please Mrs
Butler' was the winner of the
Signal Poetry Award. Once
again the collection takes
school as its subject and
invites you to meet the
Mad Professor's Daughter,
be amazed at the Longest
Kiss Contest and, if you're
a hard-pressed teacher, to
sing the Mrs Butler Blues.
5-8

PLEASE MRS BUTLER
Allan Ahlberg
Puffin pb £3.99 0140314946
These witty and often
poignant poems cover all
aspects of primary school life,
from gangs in the playground
to the nit nurse, from never-
ending projects to supply
teachers. Parents, teachers
and school children alike
will recognise the pleasures
and perils of their everyday
life in this collection.
5-8

RUMBLE IN THE JUNGLE
**Giles Andreae and David
Wojtowycz**
Orchard pb £4.99 1860396607

*It's great to be a chimpanzee
Swinging through the trees
And if we can't find nuts
to eat
We munch each other's fleas!*

This could be the noisiest
collection for young
children! Each jungle animal
has their own page with a
colourful illustration and an
individual poem which fits
each of them exactly. It's
also available as a big book
for sharing.
5-8

CAUTIONARY VERSES
**Hilaire Belloc, illustrations
Quentin Blake**
Red Fox pb £4.99 0099295318
Meet Matilda (who told such
lies it made one gasp and
stretch one's eyes) and Maria
(who pulled faces) – just two
of the legendary characters in
this ever popular collection
of Belloc's comical mockery
of Victorian manners.
7+

THIS POEM DOESN'T RHYME
ed Gerard Benson
Puffin pb £3.99 0140342273
What distinguishes poetry from prose? Most children would say rhyme but Benson shows that unrhymed poetry can be exciting and entertaining. Including the work of a wide range of poets (Shakespeare and Milton alongside James Berry and Wendy Cope) this is an unusual and inspiring anthology.
8-12

I HEARD IT IN THE PLAYGROUND

FRUITS
Valerie Bloom and David Axtell
Macmillan pb £4.99
0333653122
This is a Caribbean counting poem. Beautifully illustrated as a picture book the story poem counts the fruit that one girl can eat in one day – with maybe unsurprising consequences! The unusual fruits are also usefully listed and described at the beginning.
5-8

Roald Dahl
Roald Dahl's poetry has all the ingredients which children love – wickedly funny images, brisk rhymes and surprising twists of language – and, of course, the hints of cruelty that characterise his fiction. 'Revolting Rhymes' consists of six traditional fairy tales retold in verse. In 'Dirty Beasts' Dahl creates a ghastly menagerie of creatures doing unmentionable things. 'Rhyme Stew', for older children, transforms familiar fables and rhymes into very funny and occasionally ribald verse. In all three books Quentin Blake's mischievous illustrations complement the poems perfectly.

REVOLTING RHYMES
Puffin pb £4.99 0140504230
5-8

RHYME STEW
Puffin pb £3.50 0140343652
11+

DIRTY BEASTS
Puffin pb £4.99 0140504354
5-8

FIRST POEMS
ed Julia Eccleshare
Orchard hb £8.99 1852134119
This collection will delight all young children. Bright and colourful pictures by Selina Young accompany a text which includes well-loved classics by writers like Robert Louis Stevenson and enjoyable surprises by less familiar names. An ideal gift to encourage a love of poetry for any first reader.
4+

UN DEUX TROIS – FIRST FRENCH RHYMES
ed Opal Dunn, Illustrations Patrice Aggs
Frances Lincoln pb £4.99
ISBN 071120974X
These rhymes have been illustrated so that the meaning of the songs is clear even if there is no knowledge of French. This is a gentle and fun introduction to a new language. A tape is available.

TICKLE IN YOUR TUMMY
Ed Judith Elkin and Carlton Duncan
Macdonald pb £4.99
0750016027
This is a lively collection of Black and Asian poetry and is a great reflection of the cultural mix of our world. It ranges from Caribbean nursery rhymes to verses about Hindu gods.
5-8

Brian Patten

Brian Patten is one of Britain's best known and best loved children's poets. Born in Liverpool, he left school at 15 to work as a reporter. He began writing the poetry at an early age and started his own poetry magazine 'Underdog'. His work ranges from serious and profound to the wacky and outrageous. This poem was written especially for Puffin Books 50th birthday and has never been published before. Can you find any familiar things in this poem?

The Secret Garden will never age
The tangled undergrowth remains as fresh
As when the author put down her pen
Its mysteries are as poignant now as then

On the track The Railway Children wait
Alice still goes back and forth through
the glass
In Tom's Midnight Garden time unfurls
And children still discover secret worlds

Though Time's a thief it cannot thieve
One page from the world of make believe

At the Gates Of Dawn Pan plays his pipes,
Mole And Ratty still float in awe
downstream
The weasels watch hidden in the grass
None care how quickly human years pass

Though Time's a thief it cannot thieve
One page from the world of make-believe

His latest book is the Puffin Book of Utterly Brilliant Poetry which he has edited and which is full of great illustrated poetry by ten favourite poets.

A VERY FIRST POETRY BOOK
ed John Foster
Oxford UP pb £3.50
0199160503
A book that is packed with easy to read poems about family, games, animals and monsters. The illustrations are bold and fun. This collection of poetry for the very young is the first in a series of titles which a child can follow as they grow.
5-8

CHOCOLATE BAR
Edited by John Foster
Oxford pb £7.99 0192761250
This is a heart-warming collection of rhymes for the very young from many familiar poets. They are both funny and gentle and different illustrations are used to highlight each poem individually.
4-8

POETRY PAINTBOX ANTHOLOGIES
ed John Foster
Oxford UP pbs £3.99-£4.99
This age-ranged series takes children from the Red book at nursery school to the Blue book at primary level. There are poems on every subject you can think of and all are great fun to read.
4-8

THE ORCHARD BOOK OF OPERA STORIES
Adele Geras
Orchard hb £14.99 1860392490
This lavish book tells the stories of some of the world's favourite operas; from The Magic Flute to Turandot. Each story has a different illustrator which helps to bring each opera to life individually.

Excellent extra
'A sea-serpent saw a big tanker,
Bit a hole in her side and then sank her.
It swallowed the crew
In a minute or two,
And then picked its teeth with the anchor.'

ROBOCAT
Adrian Henri
Bloomsbury pb £3.99
0747538638

Our new cat's a robot
He really is a sight
No need to feed him Whiskas
We just plug him
in at night.

This poetry is about all kinds of creatures, school-days and even a poor boy who is in love with the weather lady. It taps into the everyday thoughts of kids and will make you laugh out loud.
8-12

RHYMES FOR ANNIE ROSE
Shirley Hughes
Red Fox pb £5.99 0099464918
For children who are being introduced to poetry at a young age this picture book provides gentle rhymes about Annie Rose, Alfie's little sister, and makes ordinary life seem enchanting
5-8

THE OWL AND THE PUSSYCAT
Edward Lear, illustrations Louise Voce
Walker pb £4.99 0744531217
One of the best loved nonsense rhymes ever is marvellously enhanced by Louise Voce's simple and direct illustrations. The boat has never been so beautiful nor so pea-green, the land where the Bong-Tree grows is clearly a desirable holiday destination and the mystery of just what exactly a runcible spoon looks like is finally cleared up.
A complete nonsense verse from Edward Lear is available in hardback.
5-8

THE PUFFIN BOOK OF UTTERLY BRILLIANT POETRY

THE PUFFIN BOOK OF NONSENSE VERSE

READ ME
A Poem a Day for the National Year of Reading
Macmillan pb £5.99
0330373536

365 poems have each been given a day and the selection of poets covers everyone you can think of and more! There is so much variety that this is a collection which will last much more than a year.

7+

KINGFISHER BOOK OF COMIC VERSE
ed Roger McGough
Kingfisher pb £5.99
0862727855

Roger McGough's personal selection of comic verse is designed to provoke both the belly-laugh and the quiet smile, to incorporate all kinds of verse from the witty to the downright daft. Any anthology which can accommodate both Ezra Pound and Monty Python is bound to include something for every taste.

8-12

LUCKY
Roger McGough
Puffin pb £3.50 0140361723

McGough's unique irreverency and comic imagination never fails to please and made this collection a successful Waterstone's Book of the Month and a real favourite with children.

9-12

THE RING OF WORDS
ed Roger McGough
Faber hb £14.99
0571169600

These poems have been chosen to be relevant to children's lives. In one way or another they are about growing up and being in the world. Poems of all kinds make this a gentle, absorbing collection.

Colin McNaughton
McNaughton is well known for his entertaining children's verse as well as his storybooks. His poems are absurd mixtures of fantasy and reality; monsters, aliens, and giants abound. Some poems are scary, but most are mischievously funny.

THERE'S AN AWFUL LOT OF WEIRDOS IN OUR NEIGHBOURHOOD
Colin McNaughton
Walker pb £6.99 0744513383

An ideal introduction to McNaughton's world of rather silly verse and pictures. It would be difficult not to enjoy the antics of such curious characters as Crazy Frankie, Nosy Porker and Lemmy the Diver. And hard not to warm to the alternative version of a traditional rhyme which begins 'Monday's child is red and spotty/ Tuesday's child won't use the potty'.

5-8

SILLY VERSE FOR KIDS
Spike Milligan
Puffin pb £3.25 0140303316
Spike Milligan's inspired nonsense appeals to most children and is particularly evident in his poems. 'Silly Verse for Kids' includes, amongst other gems, the story of the Bongaloo and a moving tribute to 'English Teeth, English Teeth/Shin-ing in the Sun'.
8-12

NOW WE ARE SIX
A A Milne
Mammoth pb £4.99
0749711795
The cosy middle class world in which the books were written has long since changed beyond recognition and yet they continue to sell in large numbers and remain as popular as ever. The work of A A Milne has charmed adults and children for nearly 70 years. It does begin to look as if Christopher Robin will be six now for ever and ever.
5-8

WHEN WE WERE VERY YOUNG
A A Milne
Mammoth pb £4.99
0749711809
Milne's first, classic collection of verse for children, illustrated in colour by Ernest Shepard. In these pages Christopher Robin continues to go down to Buckingham Palace with Alice and continues to kneel at the foot of the bed. Generations of children have grown up on these delightful poems and generations will continue to do so.
5-8

THE SECRET LIVES OF TEACHERS
ed Brian Moses
Macmillan pb £3.50
0330342657
These poems reveal all those things which you always suspected that your teachers got up to when they were not in class. It's very funny.
8-12

THEY THINK IT'S ALL OVER
ed David Orme
Macmillan pb £2.99
0330353365
Football poems about training, supporting, winning and losing. All fans will be able to understand the sentiments in this collection.
8-12

THE OXFORD TREASURY OF CLASSIC POEMS
Oxford UP pb £9.99
0192761870
The nice thing about this anthology is that it consists of classic poems from poets old and new. The poems are also of different lengths and

THE PUFFIN BOOK OF UTTERLY BRILLIANT POETRY

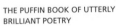

mood which makes it a lovely collection to dip into whenever you can.
8-12

BOOK OF 20TH CENTURY VERSE
ed Brian Patten
Puffin pb £6.99 0140322361
Probably the definitive anthology of twentieth century poetry for children. The book starts with contemporary poets and moves back to the beginning of the twentieth century. The reader is taken on a journey through time – and poetry – from John Agard and Michael Rosen to Walter De La Mare and Thomas Hardy.

THAWING FROZEN FROGS
Brian Patten
Puffin pb £3.99 0140342710
An outrageous collection of comic and serious poems, a sequel to the successful 'Gargling with Jelly'. In it you can meet the Teachercreature and the Utter Butter Nutter, learn about the strange disease called Schoolitis and discover why toads look much more serious than frogs.
9-12

MICHAEL ROSEN'S BOOK OF NONSENSE
Michael Rosen, illustrated by Clare Mackie
Macdonald hb £9.99
0750021926
Poems, wordplay and limericks are combined with crazy pictures. Unravelling all the meanings is only part of the appeal of this nonsense book.
8-12

WALKING THE BRIDGE OF YOUR NOSE
Ed Michael Rosen
Kingfisher pb £7.99
ISBN 0753401495
Silly sounds and crazy meanings - this is a really entertaining book. Fun, colour and nonsense.
5-8

THE SPOT ON MY BUM
Gez Walsh
King's England Press £3.99
1872438105
These poems ooze with playground humour; they are filled with all the horrible, revolting themes that children love. Read them and laugh – they are outrageous!
8+

I LIKE THIS POEM
ed Kaye Webb
Puffin pb £4.99 0140312951
This deservedly popular anthology, compiled by a former editor of Puffin Books, was the first to ask children to nominate their own poems for inclusion. The result is an eclectic choice that combines the traditional with the contemporary.
8-12

FIRST POEMS

PUFFIN BOOK OF NONSENSE VERSE
Quentin Blake
Puffin pb £5.99 0140366601
A riotous and absurd feast of nonsense, compiled by Quentin Blake and illustrated in his unique style. Edward Lear and Lewis Carroll are present, of course, to introduce the reader to the Jumblies, the Ahkond of Swat and the Jabberwock. Other writers ask such important questions as 'Have You Ever Eaten Poodle Strudel' and warn against the dangers of bathing in Irish stew.
6+

TALKING TURKEYS
Benjamin Zephaniah
Puffin pb £3.50 0140363300
A first collection of children's poetry from the fast-talking, vibrant rap poet. These are powerful, stimulating and fun poems which tackle environmental and other issues without ever becoming solemn or pompous. In his lively rhythms Zephaniah delivers poems which speak directly to you.
9-12

Shakespeare

These books all adopt very different approaches, but are written with the aim of making Shakespeare accessible to children without losing the essence of the original works. All are excellent adaptations. These books will probably be best appreciated by more sophisticated readers.

SHAKESPEARE WITHOUT THE BORING BITS
Humphrey Carpenter
Viking pb £5.99
0670855340
Humphrey Carpenter brings together some of Shakespeare's best known works and retells them as they have never been told before. Brought totally up to date, they are very accessible and humorous, reminding us how the themes of the plays are still relevant today.

SHAKESPEARE'S STORIES VOLUME 1
Leon Garfield
Puffin pb £10.99
0140389385
'Shakespeare Stories' are rewritten by the distinguished children's author in a more simplified manner, but with the inclusion of some of the original text. Stunning illustrations by the award winning Michael Foreman.

STORIES FROM SHAKESPEARE
Geraldine McCaughrean
Dolphin pb £3.99
1858813883
This is similar to Lamb's Tales of Shakespeare but is written in today's language. Ten of the most popular plays are re-written as accessible stories with a list of the characters and some short quotes to illustrate.

SOMETHING RICH AND STRANGE
Selected by Gina Pollinger
Illustrated by Emma Chichester Clark
Kingfisher pb £8.99
0753402955
This is a treasury of Shakespeare's verse; a celebration of his poetry with carefully chosen quotes which emphasise how accessible his language can be. The lovely pictures also help the words to come to life and make this a really beautiful book.

REFERENCE

Reference books for children have come a long way from the often dull encyclopedias of old. Today, thankfully, they are bright and encouraging, filled with colourful photographs and pictures. Useful, important information is often mixed with funny facts which fill in the gaps and create a more complete picture.

Publishers have made a concerted effort to create non-fiction picture books which children want to read. It is all a world away from school and homework.

The books range across the age groups from non-fiction picture books to detailed cross-sections of complicated machines. We have labelled the titles with ages to help you choose the right reference book for your child.

There is an astounding range of subject matter available too, which is especially helpful for school projects. There is everything from castles and space to philosophy and art to fascinate children. This is a selection of the best reference books. Watching, learning and fun combined...

THE NEW WAY THINGS WORK

Non-fiction picture books

WHY ARE ALL FAMILIES DIFFERENT?
Dorling Kindersley hb £4.99
0751356018
This has all the concise and simplified answers to children's questions including family trees, divorce, retirement and ageing. With lots of photographs this is a good series for discussing topics with children and finding out how they feel about things.

HONK! HONK!
Mick Manning and Brita Granstrom
Kingfisher pb £4.99
0753402947
A goose lands on a little girl's windowsill and takes her on a journey as it migrates north to nest for the summer. Although factual it is also a lovely story to read. There is a page of extra goose facts at the end.

WHAT'S UP?
Mick Manning and Brita Granstrom
Watts hb £8.99 0749627131
What could be higher than a person? Past the trees and skyscrapers and clouds, two children travel right up into space to see what really is up there above us. This is part of the award winning first reference series 'Wonderwise' which answer some of children's questions about the world.

THINK OF AN EEL
Karen Wallace
Illustrated by Mike Bostock
Walker pb £4.99 0744536391
Just one in the Read and Wonder series. Large pictures and just enough text to tell a child about the mysterious story of an eel's journey through life. The index at the back helps to show how a reference book works.
All 5-8

General Reference

CHILDREN'S ILLUSTRATED ENCYCLOPEDIA
Dorling Kindersley hb £29.95
0751357707
This is one of the best encyclopedias available for children. Each A-Z entry is a self-contained topic but the cross-referencing system encourages travel from one related entry to another. Illustrated with thousands of photographs and diagrams it covers a multitude of subjects.
8+

EYEWITNESS SERIES
Dorling Kindersley hb
£9.99 each
A vast series of reference titles covering a wide variety of subjects. Clear photographs and a great depth of information make these perfect additions to any library.
8+

VISUAL ENCYCLOPEDIA
Dorling Kindersley pb £7.99
0751305340
This is the kind of encyclopedia that everyone has always needed; the facts and all the pictures to show you exactly what it is talking about. There seems to be everything you need crammed into this little book: geographical, historical, natural and mechanical and more. You may find it shelved in the adult reference section as well.
8+

KINGFISHER CHILDREN'S ENCYCLOPEDIA
Kingfisher hb £30.00
0753401096
This is a clear and accessible encyclopedia. The text is presented in manageable, concise chunks and the illustrations are all annotated. Key facts are highlighted and all topics have a useful 'see also' box.
8+

MY FIRST OXFORD DICTIONARY

Oxford UP hb £7.99
0199102368

The perfect introduction to the world of words for children of five and upwards. Colourfully illustrated with examples of 1,500 words, definitions and simple grammar.
5-8

OXFORD PRIMARY SCHOOL DICTIONARY

Oxford UP hb £6.99
0199104492

There are 26,000 easy-to-understand definitions in this dictionary; it is a treasure trove of words for children of eight and upwards. There are hundreds of specially drawn illustrations to clarify meanings and whole sentences show how the words are used in context.
8+

OXFORD STUDY DICTIONARY

Oxford UP pb £4.99
0199103127

An ideal dictionary to use at school and for exams. The 45,000 headword entries include ones for specialist GCSE vocabulary and there are also 5,000 encyclopedic entries which cover countries, major cities, notable people and characters from myths and legends.

THE OXFORD ILLUSTRATED JUNIOR DICTIONARY

Oxford UP pb £6.99
0199103763

This is a colourful way for seven year olds and up to discover new words. Each word you need is highlighted in red which makes it easy to spot. The pictures illustrate the more difficult words and help to break up the page making the dictionary much less daunting for young users.
7-12

History

HORRIBLE HISTORIES
Terry Deary
Scholastic pb £3.50 - £6.99

Horrible Histories make history fun by leaving out the boring bits and concentrating on the exciting and occasionally nasty parts! The series is always informative as well as fun, the mix of text and cartoons just right. If you thought history was boring then read Horrible Histories and think again!
8+

JUNIOR CHRONICLE OF THE TWENTIETH CENTURY

Dorling Kindersley hb £25.00
0751356131

This is a month by month, year by year guide to the century with lots of colour and information on everything! There is such a wide range of subjects that it will keep any reader occupied for hours.

THE VERY BLOODY HISTORY OF BRITAIN 1945 TO NOW
John Farman
Red Fox pb £3.99 0099372215

Month by month, with the help of anecdotes and bizarre snippets of information, this takes an irreverent look at modern history. Find out when McDonald's first arrived in Britain and just who was Muffin the Mule?
12+

HISTORY OF BRITAIN

Ladybird 3.99

This series covers all the major periods of history right up to 1945. Each book has lots of illustrations and two page chapters on specific topics within the era. For children who are recently confident with their own reading this puts history within their grasp, although they may still need some help with the historical words.
5-8

YOUNG OXFORD HISTORY OF BRITAIN AND IRELAND
Oxford UP pb £12.99
0199104662

Illustrated with photographs and paintings and maps this book traces the history from ancient times through the British Empire to today, ending with an overview of the Twentieth Century . It is a really informative read and gives detailed insight into the changes and developments of Britain and Ireland over the years.
9-12

KINGS AND QUEENS
Plantagenet Somerset Fry
Dorling Kindersley hb £16.99
0751304867

This is a big royal history of England and Scotland. Each monarch has a biography and a list of the historical events which happened during their reign. It has been recently updated to include Diana, Princess of Wales.
10+

THE ILLUSTRATED HISTORY OF THE WORLD
Plantaganet Somerset Fry
Dorling Kindersley hb £25.00
0751351989

This is a really comprehensive and stimulating history book for children. The book covers all periods of history in all parts of the world. 1066 and the Battle of Hastings are still here but so too are the Chola peoples of India and the Anasazi cliff dwellers of North America who were William the Conqueror's contemporaries.
10+

Geography & Natural History

CHILDREN JUST LIKE ME
Barnabas and Anabel Kindersley
Dorling Kindersley hb £9.99
0751353272

Children from all around the world tell about their families, their countries and their lives. These personal touches together with lots of photographs bring geography to life in a way which has never been done before.
8-12

CROSS-SECTIONS CASTLE

Stephen Biesty

Stephen Biesty's international bestselling cross-section series started with Incredible Cross-Sections, published in 1992. It had taken him two and a half years to complete these wonderful illustrations and he continues to delight one and all with his skillful work.

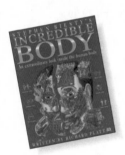

Author by author

As a boy my desire to imagine and draw was usually ignited by family outings, castles, cathedrals, steam rallies, museums, air shows and so on.

Once interested, a reference book on the subject was necessary. 'The Living World of Achievement' (Collins 1964) was my starting point with stories and pictures on 66 subjects.

I had two illustrated history books 'People of the Past' (Purnell, 1963) and 'Rulers of Britain' (Hamlyn, 1967). These gave me my first glimpse of the people who had created the things I was being taken to see. Colourful exciting pictures of the amazing things these people had designed and built were exactly what I wanted. But I wanted more. I wanted to see everything, toilets and all. So I had to draw these bits myself. I've been doing so ever since.

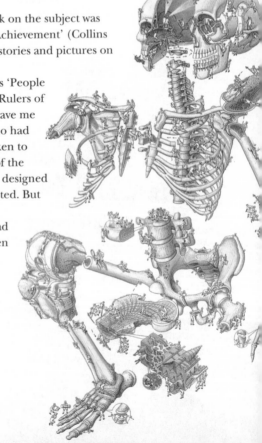

FIRST ENCYCLOPEDIA OF ANIMALS

Kingfisher hb £12.99
0753402173

This is a clearly laid-out A-Z of animals which covers hundreds of species, ecology, habitat and has step-by-step activities to find out more. Each entry has highlighted fact boxes and provides a cross-reference to similar animals. It is a great introduction to the natural world.
6-9

FIRST PICTURE ATLAS

Kingfisher pb £5.99
0753402688

There is a lot of information crammed into this book! Each country is dealt with in turn and the map is surrounded by facts on geography, animals, sports and has an 'Answer That!' challenge to make everything more interactive. The colours are bright and the text is broken up into individual topics, making it much easier to read.
5-8

KINGFISHER BOOK OF OCEANS

Kingfisher hb £14.99
0753401177

Over 250 photographs introduce the reader to the spectacular world of the oceans. Learn about storms, volcanoes and hidden underwater worlds. See weird and wonderful fish and animals. Every aspect is looked at in depth and it is both interesting and inspiring.
9-12

ZOOM IN ON...SERIES

Kingfisher hb £4.99 each

These combine reference and activity in an inspired way. A book which is small enough to fit in your pocket has a story, hundreds of facts including 'incredible but true', activities and stickers. Informative enough for projects but also ideal for things like long journeys. The topics include nature, history and real-life mysteries.
7-10

THE POP-UP GLOBE

Macmillan hb £14.99
0333732952

Open the book and an amazing 3D globe folds out in front of your eyes. The pack comes with 3 informative books on Natural Wonders, Great Cities and Wild Animals. There is also a laminated map and stickers. It is a great way to see and explore the world.
8-12

Science

INCREDIBLE CROSS-SECTIONS

Stephen Biesty
Dorling Kindersley hb £12.99
0863188079

Have you ever wanted to know where the toilets are in a space shuttle? Or maybe how many steps there are to the top of the Empire State Building? This fabulous book offers the opportunity to see inside 18 buildings and machines from a mediaeval cathedral to a Spanish Galleon. Biesty's astonishingly detailed, cutaway illustrations take the reader into the hearts of his subjects.
8+

CHEMISTRY

BEING BORN
Sheila Kitzinger
Dorling Kindersley pb £6.99
0863184219

This is the story of birth from conception to a baby's first sleep in the outside world told gently, clearly and with the most amazing photographs. It is designed to be read with a young child but is fascinating for everyone.

NEW WAY THINGS WORK
David Macaulay
Dorling Kindersley hb £19.99
0751356433

This break-through science book revolutionised the way machinery was explained to children; it uses a friendly mammoth to tell them what links a car tyre to a parachute and that a dentist's drill is a direct descendant of the first windmill. This is brand new edition and includes the latest digital technology and 27 new inventions. Fabulous illustrations clarify everything.

UNDERSTANDING THE FACTS OF LIFE
Susan Meredith
Usborne pb £7.50
0860208516

A sane and direct book which tackles tricky subjects without fuss. The book is divided into two sections, one on Growing Up and one on Babies, and with its combination of humorous illustration and instructive diagrams, it should go a long way towards informing the young reader and relieving many of their anxieties.

THE TERRIFIC TIMES TABLES BOOK
Kate Petty and Jennie Maizels
The Bodley Head hb £12.99
0370324447

It is hard to know whether this should be included in Reference or Fun and Games. At last there is a book which makes the learning of tables imaginative and fun. Lift the flaps and turn the wheels and look out for extra tips from Trixie Trick. Everyone will know their tables in no time!

HOW YOUR BODY WORKS
Usborne pb £4.99 0746023006
Where does food go? How do fingers work? How many bones do you have? These are three of the many questions answered by this entertaining but informative book which uses ingenious illustrations and everyday analogies that children will understand to explain the complicated functions of the body.

USBORNE ILLUSTRATED DICTIONARY OF SCIENCE
Usborne pb £9.99 086020989X
Divided into three main branches of science – physics, chemistry and biology – this is a densely illustrated book which contains all the key concepts and terms. Thematically arranged so that words are defined in the context of related terms,

THE NEW WAY THINGS WORK

the book also has a comprehensive index and is reliable both as a reference work and as a revision aid up to GCSE level.

MOST AMAZING POP-UP SCIENCE BOOK
Jay Young
Watts hb £14.99 0749614811
This unique example of the astonishing feats of paper engineering means that you can create working models to take you on a fascinating tour of scientific discovery. Hear a record play Edison's original recording, focus on minute details with the pop-up microscope and capture images on the screen of the camera obscura. A multi-award winner

Art & Music

WHAT THEY DON'T TELL YOU ABOUT... MUSIC
Nicola Barber
Hodder pb £3.99 0340689951
Cartoons, history, quizzes, composers, instruments and pop. Everything you need to know with lots of quirky extras to make it more interesting. Just one in a series.

ART SCHOOL
Mick Manning and Brita Granstrom
Kingfisher pb £5.99
0753401045
Designed for aspiring young artists who want to learn but also want to have a go themselves. Various kinds of art are described and each one has a suggested project to go with it. Extra tips and glossaries make this a perfect reference activity book.

CHILD'S BOOK OF ART
Lucy Micklethwait
Dorling Kindersley hb £9.99
0751350702
A striking combination of words and pictures, this book uses fine reproductions of well-known and not so well-known paintings to illustrate a child's first words. Colours are represented by paintings by David Hockney, Picasso, Matisse and Lucas Cranach, the seasons by Monet, Van Gogh, Millais and Bruegel. The result is a charming and eye-opening book.

THE YOUNG OXFORD BOOK OF THE CINEMA
David Parkinson
Oxford UP pb £9.99
0199100993
This book not only tells you the history of the moving picture but also describes the lifecycle of a film from the initial idea to the opening night. The chapters look at

different kinds of story as well as the failures and successes of actors and directors. Everything you need to know about film is here.

THE ULTIMATE 3-D POP-UP ART BOOK
Ron van der Meer and Frank Whitford
Dorling Kindersley hb £15.99
0751357332
Discover the truth about art for yourself in this amazing interactive book. Use the pop-ups to find out how people picture reality and pull-the-tabs to see how mixed primary colours reach tertiary shades. There are more than 60 works of art to see and an activity book to do your own projects at home.

Excellent Extras
The first song to be played on the first record player (called a phonograph in those days) was Mary had a Little Lamb.

Religion

THE BIBLE STORYBOOK
Georgie Adams
Dolphin pb £6.99 1858812143
This book has all the best known stories with big pictures and simplified, clear writing making it a good book both for reading to a child or sharing with a young reader.

OUT OF THE ARK
Anita Ganeri
Macdonald pb £7.99
0750026677

This is a selection of stories from the world's religions broken up into topics from birth and marriage to the adventures of war. It shows how themes recur throughout religions and provokes thought while the illustrations spark the imagination. The book ends with Fact Files on each religion and a list of who's who.

THE CHILDREN'S ILLUSTRATED BIBLE
Dorling Kindersley hb £15.99
075135113X

Selina Hastings retells all the best loved stories from both the Old and New Testament. They are further brought to life with extra facts about living in Biblical times down the sides of the pages. Her version brings out the poetry and drama for younger children.

Excellent Extras
Happy Birthday !
The eyewitness guides are 10 years old. Book number 100 is called Future and looks at amazing predictions in the world.

Russell Ash's Top 5 Facts:
1. Shooting live birds with bows and arrows was an event in the 1920 Olympics.
2. Rats are not mentioned in the Bible.
3. The shortest war on record was between Britain and Zanzibar in 1896 and lasted 38 minutes (Britain won)
4. In 1943 the chairman of IBM predicted the worldwide demand for computers would be 5!
5. The play 'The Lady of Lyons' failed to make its own first night in1888 – the safety curtain jammed.

FUN AND GAMES AND THINGS TO DO

SAM PLANTS A SUNFLOWER
Kate Petty and Axel Scheffler
Macmillan hb £4.99
ISBN 0333682599

A simple nature story with flaps to lift to discover how seeds grow. There is a big pop up sunflower and there are seeds supplied to grow your flowers.

INCREDIBLE CROSS-SECTIONS

FANTASTIC RAINY DAY BOOK
Angela Wilkes
Dorling Kindersley hb £8.99
ISBN 075135256X
60 great things to do indoors. Each activity has a list of the things you need and a step by step guide. You may never have time to go outside again! There is also a Great Games book in the same series.
5-9

AMAZING ANTHONY ANT
Lorna and Graham Philpott
Dolphin pb £4.99
ISBN 1858812844
'The ants came marching in a line hurrah, hurrah..' Sing the song and fill in the gaps by lifting the flaps on each page. Use the maze to find the way to the next page and verse. There are hours of singing and fun to have.
5-8

WHERE'S WALLY
Martin Handford
Walker pb £4.99
ISBN 0744510996
What started as a simple, ingenious idea, has become an international phenomenon, and now all children know how to find Wally, Wenda and others in these closely populated pictures. Enjoy the visual jokes and intricate detail in these compulsive and increasingly complex books.

Cunningly, in the new editions Wally has moved so everyone can start all over again!
6+

Puzzle Stories
These are good stories for reluctant readers and require plenty of interaction throughout. Highly illustrated, the clues need to be solved to work out the mysteries. Both Usborne and Walker have graded levels for skill and reading ability.

Try these:

PUZZLE WORLD
Usborne pb £6.99 0746007310
6-8 (three puzzles included)

THE WONDERFUL JOURNEY OF CAMERON CAT
Marjorie Newman
Walker pb £4.99 0744560527
6-8 (skill level 1)

CURSE OF THE LOST IDOL
Graham Round
Usborne pb £3.50
074600012X
9-12

ESCAPE FROM BLOOD CASTLE
Graham Round
Usborne pb £3.50 0860209504
9-12

THE MAGIC GLOBE
Heather Maisner
Walker pb £4.99 0744543843
9-12 (skill level 3)

DRAGON QUEST
Usborne pb £4.99
ISBN 0746023456
Along the same lines as the puzzle stories this is a fantasy adventure to solve. There are amazing illustrations and strange creatures to outwit.
9-12

THE MAZE BOOKS
Juliet and Charles Snape
Red Fox pb £4.99-£5.99
Big, detailed scenes and amazing mazes to fascinate. The series includes The Two Way Maze Book and the new Giant Book of Scary Mazes.
6+

THE KIDS ROUND THE WORLD COOKBOOK
Deri Robins
Kingfisher pb £4.99
ISBN 0753402742
Great fun preparing meals from around the world. Straightforward instructions are combined with facts, handy tips and bright illustrations.
7+

ROALD DAHL'S REVOLTING RECIPES

illustrated by Quentin Blake
Red Fox pb £6.99 0099263076
This is a great chance to create havoc in the kitchen by making the food which is familiar to everyone from Roald Dahl's stories. Some recipes are harder than others and help may be needed.
8+

101 AMAZING THINGS TO DO WITH YOUR COMPUTER

Kingfisher hb £12.99
0753401681
The best digital rainy day book. This book will show you how to get the best out of your computer and how to make exciting and useful things. Comes with a CD.
7+

ACTIVATORS SERIES

Hodder pb £3.99
Useful little paperbacks packed full of information and tips on all kind of activities. They tell you about all the central things which are vital to your hobby. There is a wide range of topics from sports and crafts to science and the internet. Something for everyone.
9+

FOUL FOOTBALL

Michael Coleman
Scholastic pb £3.99
0590190989
This is a hugely popular book from 'The Knowledge' series. Football is studied from a humorous angle; great gags, cartoons and bizarre information which is unlikely to be found anywhere else. Written by the writer of many football stories.
9+

THE GOLDFISH ATE MY KNICKERS

Caroline Plaisted
Bloomsbury pb £3.99
ISBN 0747526249
Perfect excuses for all occasions. Find out if you are an angel or not. Get ideas for excuses to use on parents, teachers and for any sudden mishaps!
8+

YOUNG ENTHUSIASTS SERIES

Dorling Kindersley £5.99-£8.99
Clear complete guides to learning all about and developing all the skills in all kinds of activities. The series includes riding, dancing, tennis and swimming. They will make anyone an expert about their hobby.
8+

ART ATTACK

Neil Buchanan
Dorling Kindersley hb £9.99
0751356263
Foolproof step by step instructions to make great arty things out of bits and pieces at home. Masks, castles, models and jewellry just to name a few. Hours of fun.
8+

DRAW 50 SERIES

Kingfisher £4.99
Step by step guides to drawing. They are great for children who want to develop their skills or for those who lack confidence. Titles include Animals, Dinosaurs and Creepy Crawlies.

Joke Books
The best of books to keep you laughing...

HA HA BONK BOOK
Janet and Allan Ahlberg
Puffin pb £3.99 0140314121

THE ALIEN JOKE BOOK
Corgi pb £3.99 0552545627

ELEPHANTASTIC!
Kingfisher pb £2.99
1856973190

THE WHOLE JOKE BOOK
Janet and Peter Hogarth
Bloomsbury pb £3.50
0747528322

Young Adult

YOUNG ADULTS

"Living your life is a long and dodgy business and stories and books help. Some help you with the living itself. Some help you just take a break. The best do both at the same time."
Anne Fine

The general impression about books for 12-15 year olds is that they are either trash series fiction or angst-driven, growing up guides or severe, issue-based, gruelling tales.

The truth is that they are all of these things and more. The majority of them are great reads but it is possible to have a balance between them all. Series fiction provides a necessary escape from school and social pressures; a relaxing leisure activity. The growing up books and social issue stories explore feelings and emotions like death, sexuality and war in a clear and unembarrassed way. They help readers to formulate opinions for real life.

The following titles introduce a wide range of quality books by a variety of authors who write with very different styles. There is a story for everyone to curl up with. Use them to discover great books written specially for this age group.

Finally, there is a selection of the best of teenage health and lifestyle books and a list of further reading which offers a tantalising glimpse of the world of adult fiction.

THE LIFE AND LOVES OF ZOE T CURLEY

THE COCKATRICE BOYS
Joan Aiken
Puffin pb £4.99 0141300108
Dangerous monsters have arrived in Britain and they are driving people underground. The Cockatrice Boys are a small army who go above ground to try to fight. This is a fantastical tale full of the suspense and intrigue that only Joan Aiken can weave.

Excellent Extras
David Almond on Skellig
"I had wanted to write a children's novel for years but didn't have the right story. Then this one came fully formed into my head. I look at this book and I think where did that come from? Almost as if it was written by someone else but obviously it came from somewhere inside me."

SKELLIG
David Almond
Hodder Signature £4.99
0340716002
Michael finds a strange man in the old garage. Although the man is frail and lives on mice and chinese takeaways, it seems that he may be an angel. Can this be possible? Whatever he is he needs to be helped because the garage is about to be demolished. All

kinds of magical experience and special relationships are in this amazing story.

FOREVER
Judy Blume
Pan pb £3.99 0330285335
Michael and Katharine's story of first love and first sex, still controversial due to its description of first sexual encounter. Almost a cult novel, it does offer some advice for young people just starting on the road to sexual independence.

TIGER EYES
Judy Blume
Pan pb £3.50 0330269542
Davey moves to New Mexico after her father is murdered during a raid on his store, and lives a life full of anger and resentment until she meets the mysterious Wolf, who shows her that life can begin again. A moving and keenly observed portrait of someone dealing with the death of a loved one.

THE FATED SKY
Henrietta Branford
Hodder Signature pb £3.99
034066102X
Ran is alone after a Viking raid kills her family but she continues to travel to take part in the winter sacrifice. Her destiny and love is a travelling musician but she

may never reach this if the evil and cruel forces have their way. This is an epic read.

JUNK
Melvin Burgess
Puffin pb £4.99 0140380191
Tar and Gemma run away to the city; he to escape abuse at home and she because her parents dislike Tar and restrict her too much. Maybe she just wants more from life. Together they enter an exciting world of new friends, crime and drugs and everything is brilliant. For a while. Until it's time to come down. This is a compulsive, involved read.

WEIRDO'S WAR
Michael Coleman
Orchard pb £4.99 1860392318
Daniel gets bullied at school by Tozer. There seems to be no escape when they are teamed up together on a school adventure holiday. After an accident, bully and victim are trapped together underground. This story is real, exciting and considers the unusual idea that bullies come in all shapes, sizes and ages.

I AM THE CHEESE
Robert Cormier
Collins pb £3.99 0006717667
Adam's journey to visit his
father in hospital becomes
a sinister psychological
odyssey. A gripping, but
pessimistic thriller which
examines the destruction
of a young boy's mind under
political interrogation.

CHASING REDBIRD
Sharon Creech
Macmillan pb £3.99
0330342134
Zinny Taylor is surrounded
by family and when she
discovers an overgrown
trail it seems like a good
opportunity to escape and
investigate at the same time.
But family and trail are
intertwined and as she
uncovers the trail the
mysteries are gradually
revealed. A good and
involving story of passions
and journeys.

WALK TWO MOONS
Sharon Creech
Macmillan £3.99 0330330004
As she travels from Ohio to
Idaho, Salamanca Hiddle
tells the story of the grief in
her life, a pain she will have
to confront at the journey's
end. A beautifully written
book, full of humour, pathos
and the power of love.

PICTURES IN THE DARK
Gillian Cross
Oxford pb £5.99 0192717413
Peter Luttrell is a weirdo.
Everyone in the school knows
it. Charlie has taken a strange
photograph of something
swimming in the river and
Peter is obsessed with it and
Charlie is determined to find
out why. This is a tense and
gripping story.

THE GREAT AUTOMATIC
GRAMMATIZATOR
Roald Dahl
Puffin pb £5.99 0140379150
This is a new collection of
Roald Dahl's short stories
specially chosen to introduce
his adult writing to younger
readers. The subtle, amusing
and often disturbing themes
which delight children are
expanded in this book.

DAUGHTER OF THE SEA
Berlie Doherty
Puffin pb £3.99
ISBN 0140379517
Drawing on mythology from
Iceland, Scotland and Ireland
this beautiful story tells the
consequences for a small
community when a couple
refuse to give a child they
have aquired back to the sea;
her real home. A timeless
fairy tale.

DEAR NOBODY
Berlie Doherty
Collins pb £3.99 0006746187
Chris and Helen's teenage
lives are shattered when
Helen discovers she is
pregnant. Helen begins a
diary to the baby - Nobody -
and Chris writes his thoughts
in beautifully told and
revealing entries which
tell much about the fragile
nature of teenage lives
and loves.

MADAME DOUBTFIRE
Anne Fine
Puffin pb £4.50 0140373551
Madame Doubtfire is the
cleaning lady with a lot more
up her sleeve as the Hillard
family discover! A black
comedy telling of the
absurdities of divorce.

THE TULIP TOUCH
Anne Fine
Puffin pb £4.99
ISBN 0140378081
Tulip seems to have no
friends until she meets
Natalie. Tulip's behaviour is
terrible, she unnerves people
with her games, she seems
insane, but Natalie finds her
exciting. Until, that is, Tulip
begins to turn on her as well.

THE POWERHOUSE
Ann Halam
Dolphin pb £3.99 1858813794
The powerhouse is a derelict building and it is perfect for practising with the band. But there is a strange feeling there, a haunting. The band try to find out the history of the powerhouse and the identity of the ghost but then they enter the real nightmare. Scary and chilling.

SECOND STAR TO THE RIGHT
Deborah Hautzig
Walker pb £3.99 0744520665
Leslie seems to be a healthy, well-adjusted, normal 14 year old. Good school and friends, everything seems fine but she is unhappy. Surely being thinner would make her life perfect. This is the compelling account of the grip of anorexia nervosa.

THE FROZEN WATERFALL
Gaye Hicyilmaz
Faber pb £3.99 0571171613
A novel charting a hunger for knowledge which is invaded by political circumstance. Unusual, often moving, it reflects at length upon the fight for personal freedom during a Turkish family's move to Switzerland.

THE OUTSIDERS
S E Hinton
Collins pb £3.99 0006722253
A rites of passage novel of gang life and academic ambition. Often violent but always entertaining, it raises questions about justice, prejudice and the way people respond to poverty. Written when Hinton was a teenager herself in the 60's. It has become a cult classic.

MAPHEAD
Lesley Howarth
Walker pb £3.99 0744536472
The need to belong is explored powerfully in this original novel of Boothe and Powers (visitors from the subtle world) and their gypsy existence on earth. Strange and compelling.

A DIFFERENT LIFE
Lois Keith
Livewire pb £5.99 0704349469
Libby Starling is excited about her school trip. But it's about to change her life. After swimming in the sea she becomes mysteriously ill. Everyone around her has their own idea of what is good for her but Libby needs to find her own strength in order to live the different life that is best for her.

GODHANGER
Dick King-Smith
Corgi pb £3.99 0552545015
The Skymaster watches over Godhanger Wood and sees the innocent bloodshed that happens. When the birds in the wood decide to save themselves the gamekeeper is locked in a battle of wills with the Skymaster- the most deadly fight of all.

THE TWELFTH DAY OF JULY
Joan Lingard
Puffin pb £3.99 0140371753
The first in the Kevin and Sadie Belfast tales. One night Kevin and his Catholic friends sneak into 'Protestant country' and deface a mural, enraging Sadie and her friends. This starts off a series of incidents which culminate in tragedy on the 12th July.

A LITTLE LOVE SONG
Michelle Magorian
Mammoth pb £3.99 0749410616
It is 1943 and, evacuated to a sleepy seaside town, Rose and Diane are, for the first time, free of adult restrictions. Both girls begin a summer of self-discovery in this touching story of independence and first love.

Sharon Creech

Before Sharon Creech was a writer for children she did lots of 'deadly boring' things. Now she is an award winning author. This is her account of why she started to write.

Author by author

"Journeys have also been important to me. When I was young, my family took a car trip each summer, and the one we took when I was thirteen – from Ohio to Idaho, nearly 3000 miles in the car – was particularly dramatic. What a vast and varied country! I wanted to memorise everything I saw or heard. That journey was later recreated in Walk Two Moons, and I loved every minute of travelling with Salamanca across the States.

To me, every book, whether I'm writing or reading it, is a journey. Each book is a chance to travel along with the characters, and to discover what matters to them, and how their journeys change them. I am intrigued by the way physical journeys (from this place to that place) mirror interior journeys – how we are changed and shaped by where we go, who we meet, and what we think along the way."

Some books by Sharon Creech:

Walk Two Moons
Chasing Redbird
Absolutely Normal Chaos

published by Macmillan

THE CHANGEOVER
Margaret Mahy
Puffin pb £4.50 0140372954
This many-layered blend of supernatural thriller and romantic novel explores the complexities of family ties and loyalty as Laura goes through her 'changeover' into a witch in order to save her possessed brother, and encounters the mysterious, intense Sorry Carlisle.

THEY DO THINGS DIFFERENTLY THERE
Jan Mark
Red Fox pb £3.50 0099264218
A group of individual portraits drawn together to form a stunning tale. An inspired account of two teenagers who appear not to fit into the world around them. Yet once you take a closer look at that world, is it any surprise..?

HATCHET
Gary Paulsen
Macmillan pb £3.99
0330310453
When a small plane crashes in the Canadian wilderness, 13 year-old Brian has to quickly learn how to survive, the hard way. A gripping, heart-stopping story of a boy's fight to survive under extreme circumstances.

NORTHERN LIGHTS
Philip Pullman
Scholastic pb £4.99
0590139614
Lyra's adventure begins when her friend Roger disappears. With only her daemon to keep her company she sets out to find him. She moves north to bleak frozen lands where armoured bears rule and witch queens fly. Lyra is in the middle of terrible things and will have to fight hard to escape. This is a tense and gripping fantasy.

THE BUTTERFLY TATTOO
Philip Pullman
Macmillan pb £3.99
0300368567
Chris falls in love with Jenny the first time he sees her. Fate has brought her to him and it will be fate which ultimately drives their love down a road of betrayal and danger. Truth and trust are complex issues in this story where the cruel twists surround the characters and readers can only read on with their hearts in their mouths as it reaches the climax.

OLIVIA
Rosie Rushton
Picadilly pb £5.99 185340411X
Olivia's dad has run off, her boyfriend has dumped her, her best friend has moved schools and her mother has taken in a lodger. But at least there is gorgeous Ryan to take her mind off her problems! Rosie Rushton knows how a teenager feels.

Robert Swindells

Swindells is a well-established author with an enviable history of successful and award-winning books to his name. Stepping into the minds of young people with apparent ease and psychological insight, he never shies away from difficult issues.

STONE COLD
Robert Swindells
Puffin pb £3.99 0140362517
Link runs away to London to escape his stepfather and ends up living rough on the streets, where he encounters a frightening and dangerous world. A powerful, chilling and disturbingly realistic examination of our attitudes to the homeless.

ROLL OF THUNDER HEAR MY CRY
Mildred D Taylor
Puffin pb £5.99 0140371745
Set in the American deep south in the 1930's and 1940's, this book follows the lives of Cassie Logan and her family as they struggle against racism, oppression and financial hardships to retain their land, their lives and their dignities.

GHOST STORY
Julian F. Thompson
Bloomsbury £4.99 0747536600
Anna moves to an old country inn where she meets Roxy the two hundred year old ghost. Even Anna thinks this is a bit strange but they become friends. Then Tony the good-looking photographer arrives and wants Anna to help him with some of his shots. Roxy has her suspicions but will she be able to persuade Anna before things go too wrong? A good read with an exciting finish.

THE LIFE AND LOVES OF ZOE T. CURLEY
Martin Waddell
Walker pb £3.99 0744554896
Welcome to the life of Zoe T. Curley. This is her diary of family issues and, more importantly, BOYS and LOVE. Join her and her best friend Melissa in this story of the trials of teenage life.

JUSTICE OF THE DAGGER
James Watson
Puffin pb £4.99 0141300078
Muyu and Lyana are determined to stop the destruction of the rainforest and to protect the tribe that lives there. But they need to fight the ruthless government. A tough political thriller.

FALLING INTO GLORY
Robert Westall
Mammoth pb £4.99 0749717556
A romp through love and rugby in a Northern school during the 1950's. Westall treats the subject of love between pupil and teacher with a wry sensitivity and sometimes uncomfortable realism.

MAKE LEMONADE
Virginia Euwer Wolff
Faber pb £4.99 0571175066
Thoughts from a fourteen year old girl who ponders the frailties and bad choices made by those around her. Written in an unsentimental fashion it gives insight into the demands of life and draws you in.

Z FOR ZACHARIAH
Robert O'Brien
Collins pb £3.99 0006710816
Ann has to come to terms with being the sole survivor of a nuclear holocaust. However, her solitude is interrupted by an apparently sinister man. The book takes the form of Ann's diary and is both mysterious and compassionate.

Teenage series

Series fiction for young adults has moved on from the days of mass marketed popular fiction of Sweet Valley High and Point Horror. Publishers now use labelling as a way of highlighting their own teenage fiction - an emphasis on quality fiction with a range of writers. Often they are filed under the relevant author on the shelves and the generic covers just help a buyer to identify a list of books that has been enjoyed previously.

Point series

Published by Scholastic 'Point' has become the overall name for what is really an industry of generic fiction, ranging from crime and science fiction to the phenomenally successful

Point Horror series. American in origin and using different authors (look out for good ones like Diane Hoh), Point play at being adult books but are actually fairly safe reads with an overall moral tone. Look out for the more literary fiction on the 'Scholastic Press' label; good reads but with more depth.

Hodder Signature

Some of the books already reviewed are published under this imprint. The list of titles features writing from new and established authors. Although each novel offers its own strengths all the stories are engrossing and thought-provoking.

Contents series

Published by Egmont Children's Books, these books are for readers who want to explore the world through characters of their own age or older. They aim to make the experience of life a less isolating journey through a range of topics. Everyone will find a story to relate to.

Non-Fiction

TEENAGE WORRIER'S GUIDE TO LIFE
Ros Asquith
Transworld pb £4.99
0552145343
Introducing 15 year-old Letty Chubb, typical teenage worrier. Following her diary of angst and anguish here is her guide to life to take you through to the 21st Century. An A-Z list of things to consider from Appearances to Vegetarians this book provides a painfully funny and accurate insight into troubled teenage life.

EVERYBODY ELSE DOES! WHY CAN'T I?
Yvonne Coppard
Puffin pb £3.99 0140375392
Two hilarious diaries of a teenage girl and her mother. How will Cathy cope with her exams and her mother's mysterious behaviour? And how will her mother cope with the changing family?

BULLYING
Michele Elliott
Hodder Wise Guides pb £3.99
0340714832
This book takes time to say that bullying is something that can happen to anyone at anytime and discusses what to do if it is happening to you. It has practical advice, discusses how to make friends and

respect yourself and even how to change if you are the bully yourself.

ZLATA'S DIARY
Zlata Filipovic
Puffin pb £3.99 0140374639
The diary of 13 year-old Zlata is, perhaps, the most moving account of the war in former Yugoslavia. In it she describes the changes to her home in Sarajevo in 1992. As harrowing as Anne Frank's diary, this account at least ends in escape to Paris for Zlata.

LIVING WITH A WILLY
Nick Fisher
Macmillan pb £4.99
ISBN 0330332481
A lighthearted approach to puberty for boys. Full of illustrations it is funny and informative.

THE DIARY OF ANNE FRANK
Anne Frank
Puffin pb £4.99 0140385622
The famous diary of a young girl in war-torn Amsterdam, who heroically saves lives in her cramped attic. Entries of childlike spontaneity are mixed with passages of startling maturity, reflection, optimism and wit.

WHAT'S THE BIG IDEA?

Hodder pbs £3.99

A huge range of topics are covered in this series: Women's Rights, Virtual Reality, Religion and Animal Rights just to mention a few. They tell you what you need to know on the issues which concern people most without the boring extras.

HAVE YOU STARTED YET?

Ruth Thomson

Macmillan pb £3.99

0330333722X

A friendly and straight forward guide to all aspects of periods. This illustrated book successfully tackles all the questions raised during a time of increasing self-awareness and personal change.

What To Read Now

The move from the safety of the children's book to the enormous and sometimes intimidating adult book world can be difficult for even the most confident readers. Here are some good books and authors to start with:

General fiction

Prime of Miss Jean Brodie
By Muriel Spark

Crow Road
By Iain Banks

Tales of the City
By Armistead Maupin

A Prayer for Owen Meany
By John Irving

Anita and Me
By Meera Syal

The Zigzag Kid
By David Grossman

Paddy Clarke Ha Ha Ha
By Roddy Doyle

Behind the Scenes at the Museum
By Kate Atkinson

White Merc With Fins
By James Hawes

Are you Experienced
By William Sutcliffe

Crime fiction

Ruth Rendell
Colin Dexter
Raymond Chandler
Patricia Cornwell

Science fiction

Iain M. Banks
Douglas Adams
Terry Pratchett
Robert Rankin

Biography

Jung Chang
Laurie Lee
Roald Dahl
Maya Angelou

Poetry

Simon Armitage
Wendy Cope
Carol Ann Duffy
John Hegley

Services at Waterstone's

Recommendation

Our booksellers really know and care about what they are selling. If you need help, please don't hesitate to ask. We also select 3 of the best new titles each month, to reflect various age-groups, for our Waterstone's Recommends promotion. For the duration of the month you will receive 20% discount on each title.

Writers at Waterstone's

Ask at your branch for details of author events (including children's events).

Waterstone's Mailing Service

Waterstone's mail order facility: Waterstone's Mailing Service, 4-5 Milsom Street, Bath BA1 1DA

Booksearch

Waterstone's Booksearch service will try to track down out-of-print books for you. Booksearch, 32-40 Calverley Road, Tunbridge Wells, TN1 2TD

Website

www.waterstones.co.uk

Signed First Editions

A choice of up to 150 of the year's finest fiction and non-fiction titles – all signed by the author and posted to you. Waterstone's Signed First Editions Collection, 4-5 Milsom Street, Bath BA1 1DA

Waterstone's Book Vouchers

Accepted in over 200 bookshops in the United Kingdom and Ireland, including all branches of Waterstone's and Dillons, as well as all branches of HMV.

Subject index

Here are some suggestions for books and authors which might help you with special interests or needs.

Abuse
Junk
I am the Cheese
The Outsiders
Stone Cold

Adoption & Fostering
Anne Of Green Gables
Back Home
Bad Girls
Ballet Shoes
Goodnight Mr Tom
Great Elephant Chase
The Demon Headmaster
The Story Of Tracey Beaker

Adventure (see also Thrillers)
Asterix
Demon Headmaster
Gary Paulsen
Harry Potter
Hiding Out
Jack Black And The Ship Of Thieves
Robin Of Sherwood
Saga Of Erik The Viking
Swallows And Amazons
The Great Elephant Chase
The Hundred-Mile-An-Hour Dog
Tintin
Willard Price

Anger
George's Marvellous Medicine
Goggle Eyes
I Don't Want To
Matilda
The Magic Finger

Animals
Animal Ark
Beatrix Potter
Brian Jacques
Dick King-Smith
Dr Xargle
Hairy McClary
Rudyard Kipling
Tarka The Otter
The Incredible Journey
The Whale's Song
The Wind In The Willows
Watership Down
Willard Price

Babies
Dr Xargle
Janine & The New Baby

Mummy Laid An Egg
Peepo
So Much
Understanding The Facts Of Life

Ballet
Ballet Shoes
Ballet Stories
Orchard Book Of Stories From The Ballet
Scrambled Legs

Bullying
Blubber
Bully
Krindlekrax
Matilda
The Diddakoi
Wierdo's War
Willy The Wimp

Computers & Technology
Hacker
101 amazing things to do with your computer

Death & Bereavement
Badger's Parting Gifts
Charlotte's Web
Girls In Love
Goodnight Mr Tom
Granpa
The Diddakoi
The Secret Garden
Two Weeks With The Queen
Walkabout

Divorce & Single Parent Families
Goggle Eyes
Josie Smith
Madame Doubtfire
The Man Whose Mother Was A Pirate
The Suitcase Kid

Eating Problems & Disorders

Blubber
Oliver's Vegetables
They Do Things Differently
There

Environmental Issues

Brother Eagle, Sister Sky
Dear Greenpeace
Dinosaurs & All That
Rubbish
Justice Of The Dagger
Oi, Get Off Our Train
The Iron Man
The Iron Woman
The Magic Finger
Watch Out For The Giant
Killers
Why The Whales Came

Fantasy

Alice In Wonderland
Beaver Towers
Box Of Delights
Dark Is Rising
Finn Family Moonintroll
His Dark Materials
Narnia Series
Peter Pan
Philip Ridley Books
Sword In The Stone
The Borrowers
The Changeover
The Haunting
The Magic Finger
The Weirdstone Of
Brisingamen
Wizard Of Earthsea

Fear (see also Phobias)

Thud
The Bear Under the Stairs
The Huge Bag of Worries
I am David

Funny Stories

David Henry Wilson
Flat Stanley
Jacqueline Wilson
Kingfisher Book Of
Funny Stories
Krindlekrax
Maurice Gleitzman
Paul Jennings
Paula Danziger
Roald Dahl
Scrambled Legs
Spot On My Bum

Gender issues

Bill's New Frock
Flour Babies
Happy Families
Karate Princess
Mildred D Taylor
Ms Wiz
Paper Bag Princess
Pippi Longstocking
Princess Smartypants
Willy The Wimp

Ghosts (see also thrillers)

Ghostly Haunts
The Haunting

Historical Periods (see also war)

Prehistory
Stig of the Dump

Vikings & Romans

Asterix
Eagle of the Ninth
The Saga of Eric the Viking

Tudors & Stuarts

Tudor Terrors

Victorians

The Secret Garden
Tom's Midnight Garden

Early 20th Century

Charlotte Sometimes
Mildred D Taylor
Wreck of the Zanzibar

Illness & Disability

A Different Life
Blabber Mouth
Dr Dog
Heidi
Pig Heart Boy
Skellig
The Secret Garden
Two Weeks With The Queen

Interactive Titles

Fantastic Maze Book
Pop Up Books
Puzzle Adventures
Very Hungry Caterpillar
Where's Wally

Irish Interest

Joan Lingard
Celtic Myths

Jealousy

Bel Mooney
Goggle Eyes
Red Eyes At Night
Titch

Loneliness & Friendship

Amber Brown Is Not A
Crayon
BFG
Charlotte's Web
My Best Friend
Pumpkin Soup

Something Else
The Friends
The Tulip Touch
Winnie The Witch

Moving Home
Amber Brown Is Not A Crayon
Back Home
Starring Sally J Freeman as Herself
Superfudge
The Bed & Breakfast Star
The Peppermint Pig
The Suitcase Kid
Walk Two Moons

Multi-Cultural Books
A Carribean Dozen
Amazing Grace
Brother Eagle, Sister Sky
Handas Surprise
Hurricane Betsy
I Am David
Janine & The New Baby
Mildred D Taylor
One Smiling Grandma
Rosa Guy
So Much
Talking Turkeys
Walkabout

Mystery Stories
Pictures in the dark

Pony Stories
Black Beauty
The Enchanted Horse

Phobias
Otherwise Known as Sheila the Great
Owl Who Was Afraid Of The Dark
The Bear Under The Stairs
Can't You Sleep Little Bear
Ewdard's First Night Away

Racism Issues
Mildred D Taylor
Rosa Guy

Reluctant Readers
(see interactive titles)
Asterix
Barrington Stoke (Publisher)
Don Quixote
Enid Blyton
Soccer At Sandford
Sweet Valley Series
The Babysitters Club
Tintin

Romance
A Little Love Song
Falling Into Glory
Forever
Girls In Love
Life And Loves Of Zoe T.Curley
Sweet Valley High

School Stories
Billy And The New School
Goalkeepers Revenge
Mr Majeika
Ms Wiz
My Teacher Is An Alien
Please Mrs Butler
The Demon Headmaster
The School At The Chalet Series
The Worst Witch

Science & technology
Rebecca's World
Russell Stannard's Books
Science Fiction
Tripods Trilogy

Scottish interest
Jinny stories
Josie Smith
Katie Morag & the Two Grandmothers

Sex & Sexuality
Are You There God, It's Me, Margaret
Dance On My Grave
Dear Nobody
Forever
Mummy Laid An Egg
Sibling Rivalry
Fudge-a-mania
Horrid Henry

Sports
Soccer At Sandford
The Big Series

Thrillers & Scary Stories
Goosebumps
Justice Of The Dagger
Oxford Book Of Scary Tales
RL Stine
Robert Cormier
Room 13
Switchers
The Tulip Touch
Tudor Terror
Whispers In The Graveyard

Travel

Around The World In 80
Days

Charlotte Sometimes

The Last Gold Diggers

Tom's Midnight Garden

Traveller In Time

War & Conflict

Back Home

Joan Lingard

Little Women

The Frozen Waterfull

The Outsiders

Z For Zachariah

Zlata's Diary

Wizards & Witches

Carbonel

Dog On A Broomstick

Meg & Mog

Mr Majeika

Ms Wiz

Simon & The Witch

The Witches

The Wizard Of Oz

The Worst Witch

Winnie The Witch

World War II

Carrie's War

Diary Of Anne Frank

Going Solo

Michelle Magorian

Robert Westall

Starring Sally J Freeman
as Herself

The Silver Sword

War Boy

When Hitler Stole Pink Rabbit

Further Resources

If you wish to seek out more
in-depth help for your child's
needs, then these
Associations may be able
to help:

Young Book Trust

Tel: 0181 516 3663

Young Book Trust Scotland

Tel: 0131 229 3663
(for special needs booklists,
author information and
general advice)

**National Library for the
Handicapped Child**

Tel: 01734 891101
(books in braille, large print,
signed language, videos of
books)

**100 Multi Cultural Picture
Books Working Group against
Racism in Children's Resources**

Tel: 0171 627 4594

Welsh Book Council

Tel: 01970 624151

**Children's Literature
Association of Ireland**

Church of Ireland College of
Education

96 Upper Rathmines Road
Dublin 6

British Dyslexia Association

98 London Road

Reading RG1 5AU

Tel: 0118 996 2677

The Poetry Library

Tel: 0171 921 0664

IBBY

Tel: 0181 392 3008
(International Board on
Books for Young People)

**Award Winning Children's
Books**

There are scores of medals
awarded for outstanding
children's books every year.
They range from
environmental awards to
awards from magazines to
awards with winners chosen
by children. We have listed
some of the more prestigious
prizes and their recent
winners below:

Carnegie Medal

**This award was established in
1936 and is awarded to an
outstanding book for
children written in English.
Early winners included Noel
Streatfield, CS Lewis, Alan
Garner and Arthur Ransome.
In recent years the prize has
received controversial
coverage for its choice of
hard-hitting winners.**

1990 Wolf
Gillian Cross

1991 Dear Nobody
Berlie Doherty

1992 Flour Babies
Anne Fine

1993 Stone Cold
Robert Swindells

1994 Whispers in the
Graveyard
Theresa Breslin

1995 Northern Lights:
His Dark Materials I
Philip Pullman

1996 Junk
Melvin Burgess

1997 Riverboy
Tim Bowler

Kate Greenaway Medal

**Established in 1955, this prize
is awarded to a children's
book illustrator for a work
published in the UK. Early
winners read like a who's who
of 20th century children's
illustrations with such names
as Edward Ardizzone, Brian
Wildsmith, Raymond Briggs,
Shirley Hughes and Helen
Oxenbury.**

1990 The Whale's Song
Gary Blythe

1991 The Jolly Christmas
Postman
Janet & Allan Ahlberg

1992 Zoo
Anthony Browne

1993 Black Ships Before Troy
Alan Lee

1994 Way Home
Gregory Rogers

1995 Christmas Miracle of
Jonathon Toomey
P.J. Lynch

1996 Baby Who Wouldn't
Go To Bed
Helen Cooper

1997 When Jessie Came
Over The Sea
P. J. Lynch

Guardian Children's Fiction Award

**Established in 1967 and
awarded to an outstanding
work of fiction for children
written by a British or
Commonwealth author. Early
winners were Joan Aiken,
Nina Bawden and Peter
Dickinson.**

1990 Goggle Eyes
Anne Fine

1991 The Kingdom by
the Sea
Robert Westall

1992 Paper Faces
Rachel Anderson

The Exiles
Hilary McKay

1993 Low Tide
William Mayne

1994 The Mennyms
Sylvia Waugh

1995 Maphead
Lesley Howarth

1996 –joint winners
Northern Lights: His Dark
Materials I
Philip Pullman

The Sherwood Hero
Alison Prince

1997 Junk
Melvin Burgess

1998 Fire Bed and Bone
Henrietta Branford

Waterstone's Children's Books of The Month

**We select three books to
reflect different reading ages.
Most of the titles chosen fall
into these age groups- 0-5, 6-8
and 9+**

1998

January

Red Eyes At Night
Michal Morpurgo

Water Wings
Morris Gleitzman

The Final Journey
Gudrun Pausewang

February

The Jealous Giant
Kaye Umansky

The Last Gold Diggers
Harry Horse

The Life And Loves Of
Zoe T Curly
Martin Waddell

March

Schnitzel Von Krumm
Lynley Dodd

Amber Brown Is Not
A Crayon
Paula Danziger

Minnow On The Say
Phillipa Pearce

April

Deep Blue Sea
Jakki Wood

Toots And The Upside
Down House
Carol Hughes

The Poetry Book
Adrian Mitchell

May

Honey Biscuits
**Meredith Hooper
& Alison Bartlett**

Art Attack
Neil Buchanan

Justice Of The Dagger
James Watson

June

Monkey Do
**Allan Ahlberg
& André Amstutz**

Young Telegraph/Just
What I Always Wanted
Ed. Alison Stanley

Young Oxford Book Of
Football Stories
James Riordan

July

Nicky
Tony & Zoe Ross

Mr. William Shakespeare's Plays
Marcia Williams

Harry Potter And The
Chamber Of Secrets
J.K. Rowling

August

The Lighthouse Keeper's
Catastrophe
Rhonda & David Armitage

Deep Down Underground
Robert Crowther

Skellig
David Almond

September

The Time It Took Tom
Nick Sharratt

The First Encyclopedia
Of Animals
**Jon Kirkwood
& John Farndon**

Pig-Heart Boy
Malorie Blackman

October

Pumpkin Soup
Helen Cooper

Squids Will Be Squids
Jon Scieszka & Lane Smith

Angela And Diabola
Lynne Reid Banks

November

Bad Habits
Babette Cole

A Year In The City
**Kathy Henderson
& Paul Howard**

The Kin
Peter Dickinson

December

The Christmas Bear
**Ian Whybrow
& Alex Scheffler**

The Lion And The Unicorn
Shirley Hughes

The Puffin Book Of Utterly
Brilliant Poetry
Ed.Brian Patten

Index

Author and title Index

Thanks to the following booksellers who offered their experience and help:
Liz Bax, Amanda Berry, Sarah Collins, Jane Davey, Sheila Denton,
Janet Forsyth, Anne Gibbs, Dani Hall, Carole Johnson, Nan Molyneux,
Natalie Moore, Linda Morison, Peter Mountford, Kate Murphy,
Lise Nefell, Katy O'Donnell, Charlotte Perry, Elizabeth Rogers,
Katie Sharpe, Kate Steele, Alison Targett, Jenny Taylor, Kate Thomson,
Lisa Westmorland, and also to the booksellers who contributed to the
first edition of this guide.

Special thanks to Mark Collison, Penny Insole, and the authors: Lucy
Cousins, Allan Ahlberg, Helen Cooper, Mary Murphy, John Burningham,
David Pelham, Colin Mcnaughton, Francesca Simon, Morris Gleitzman,
Jacqueline Wilson, Paula Danziger, J.K. Rowling, Philip Pullman, Brian
Patten, Stepen Biesty, Sharon Creech.

Grateful acknowledgement is made to the following for permission to
reproduce illustrations from their books: Illustrations from BULLY ©
1993 David Hughes:WE'RE GOING ON A BEAR HUNT Text © 1989
Michael Rosen. Illustrations © 1989 helen Oxenbury. Published by
Walker Books Ltd. London. THE VERY HUNGRY CATERPILLAR
Illustrations © Eric Carle;The Snowman Illus. © Raymond Briggs;
FAIRY TALES illus. © Michael Foreman; All published by Penguin
Books. MUMMY LAID AN EGG Illus. ©Babette Cole published by
Red Fox. THE THREE LITTLE WOLVES AND THE BAD PIG illus.
© Helen Oxenbury published by Mammoth. THE IRON MAN illus.
© Andrew Davidson; THE IRON WOMAN illus.© published by Faber
and Faber Ltd. THREADBEAR illus.© Mick Inkpen published by
HodderChildren's Books.© Barrington Stokes (publisher). BOOK
OF CREATION STORIES illus.© Louise Brierly; FIRST POEMS illus.
© Selina Young published by Orchard Books (Watts publishing Ltd).
I WANT TO BE illus.© Tony Ross; SUDDENLY illus.© Colin
McNaughton published by Harper Collins Children's Books.
Cover: THE BIG PETS illus.©Lane Smith reproduced by kind
permission of Penguin Books.

Waterstone's Branches

ABERDEEN
236 Union St
Tel: 01224 571655

ABERYSTWYTH
Great Hall
Penglais Building
University of Wales
Tel: 01970 623251

ALTRINCHAM
24 George Street
Tel: 0161 941 4040

AMSTERDAM
Kalverstraat 152
Amsterdam
The Netherlands
Tel: 00 312 0 638 3821

ASTON UNIVERSITY
12 Gosta Green
Aston Triangle
Tel: 0121 359 3242

AYLESBURY
31-32 Friars Square
Tel: 01296 423153

BASINGSTOKE
2 Castle Square
Tel: 01256 333030

BATH
4-5 Milsom St
Tel: 01225 448515

University of Bath
Claverton Down
Tel: 01225 465565

BEDFORD
11-13 Silver Street
Tel: 01234 272432

Cranfield University
Bookshop
College Road
Wharley End
Tel: 01234 754280

BELFAST
Queen's Building
8 Royal Avenue
Tel: 01232 247355

BIRKENHEAD
188/192 Grange Rd
Tel: 0151 650 2400

BIRMINGHAM
24-26 High Street
Tel: 0121 633 4353
Fax: 0121 633 4300

Birmingham University
Ring Road North
Edgbaston
Tel: 0121 472 3034

BLACKPOOL
4, The Tower Shopping
Centre
Bank Hey Street
Tel: 01253 296136

BLUEWATER PARK
(opens Spring 1999)

BOLTON
32-36 Deansgate
Tel: 01204 522588

BOURNEMOUTH
14/16 The Arcade
Tel: 01202 299449

Bournemouth
University
Talbot Campus
Fern Barrow
Poole
Tel: 01202 595528

BRADFORD
University of Bradford,
Great Horton Rd
Tel: 01274 727885

Management
Centre Bookshop,
Emm Lane
Tel: 01274 481404

The Wool Exchange
Tel: 01274 723127

BRUNEL UNIVERSITY
Cleveland Road
Uxbridge
Tel: 01895 257991

BRIGHTON
55-56 North St
Tel: 01273 327867

71-74 North Street
Tel: 01273 206017

BRISTOL
27-29 College Green
Tel: 0117 925 0511

University of Bristol
Tyndall Avenue
Tel: 0117 925 4297

Cribbs Causeway
33 Lower Level,
The Mall
Tel: 0117 950 9813

The Galleries
Broadmead
Tel: 0117 925 2274

BROMLEY
20-22 Market Sq
Tel: 0181 464 6562

BRUSSELS
Boulevard Adolphe
Max 71-75
B1000 Brussels
Belgium
Tel: 00 322 219 2708

BURY
4 Union Arcade
Tel: 0161 764 2642

CAMBRIDGE
6 Bridge St
Tel: 01223 300123
Fax: 01223 301539

CANTERBURY
20 St Margaret's St
Tel: 01227 456343

CARDIFF
2a The Hayes
Tel: 01222 665606

University of Derby
Keddleston Road
Tel: 01332 331719

CARMARTHEN
Trinity College
Tel: 01267 238100

CHELMSFORD
The Meadows Centre
High Street
Tel: 01245 493300

CHELTENHAM
88-90 The Promenade
Tel: 01242 512722

CHESTER
43-45 Bridge St Row
Tel: 01244 328040

CHICHESTER
The Dolphin and
Anchor
West Street
Tel: 01243 773030

COLCHESTER
16 Culver Precinct
Tel: 01206 767623

University of Essex
Wivenhoe Park
Tel: 01206 864773

CORK
69 Patrick St
Tel: 00 353 21 276522

Boole Library
Basement
University College
Tel: 00 353 21 276575

COVENTRY
22 Cathedral Lanes
Broadgate
Tel: 01203 227151

Coventry University
26 Earl Street
Tel: 01203 229092

Coventry University
Bookshop
Earl Street
Tel: 01203 230880

CRAWLEY
83-84 County Mall
Tel: 01293 533471

CROYDON
1063 Whitgift Centre
Tel: 0181 686 7032

DERBY
78-80 St Peter's St
Tel: 01332 296997

University of Derby
Keddleston Road
Tel: 01332 331719

Chevin Avenue
Mickelover
Tel: 01332 511462

DORKING
54-60 South St
Tel: 01306 886884

DUBLIN
7 Dawson St
Tel: 00 353 1 679 1260

The Jervis Centre
Tel: 00 353 1 878 1311

DUNDEE
35 Commercial St
Tel: 01382 200322

DURHAM
69 Saddler St
Tel: 0191 383 1488

University Bookshop
55-57 Saddler Street
Tel: 0191 384 2095

EASTBOURNE
120 Terminus Rd
Tel: 01323 735676

EDINBURGH
128 Princes St
Tel: 0131 226 2666

13-14 Princes St
Tel: 0131 556 3034/5

83 George St
Tel: 0131 225 3436

EGHAM
Royal Holloway College
Egham Hill
Tel: 01784 471272

EPSOM
113 High St
Tel: 01372 741713

EXETER
48-49 High St
Tel: 01392 218392

5 Isambard Parade
St. Davids Station
Tel: 01392 273433
Tel: 01392 491250

FOLKESTONE
1-2 Guildhall St
Tel: 01303 221 979

GATESHEAD
17 The Parade
Metro Centre
Tel: 0191 493 2715

GLASGOW
153-157
Sauchiehall St
Tel: 0141 332 9105

GUILDFORD
35-39 North St
Tel: 01483 302919

HANLEY
Stoke-On-Trent
The Tontines Centre
Parliament Row
Tel: 01782 204582

HATFIELD
University of
Hertfordshire
College Lane
Tel: 01707 284940

HEREFORD
18-20 Commercial St
Tel: 01432 275100

University of
Hertfordshire
Mangrove Road
Tel: 01707 285505

**HUDDERSFIELD
UNIVERSITY**
Queensgate
Tel: 01484 472200

HULL
University of Hull
Tel: 01482 444190

The Grand Buildings,
Jameson St
Tel: 01482 580234

ILFORD
158-160 High Road
Tel: 0181 478 8428

INVERNESS
50-52 High St
Tel: 01463 717474

IPSWICH
15-19 Buttermarket
Tel: 01473 289044

KEELE
University of Keele
Tel: 01782 627001

KETTERING
72-76 High St
Tel: 01536 481575

KING'S LYNN
76-77 High St
Tel: 01553 769934

**KINGSTON-UPON-
THAMES**
23-25 Thames St
Tel: 0181 5471221

Kingston University
2 Brook Street
Tel: 0181 546 7592

LANCASTER
2-8 King St
Tel: 01524 61477

Lancaster University
Bookshop
Bailrigg
Tel: 01524 32581

LEAMINGTON SPA
1 Priorsgate
Warwick St
Tel: 01926 883804

LEEDS
36-38 Albion St
Tel: 0113 242 0839

93-97 Albion St
Tel: 0113 244 4588

6 Gledhow Wing
St. James Hospital
Beckett Street
Tel: 0113 243 3144

LEICESTER
21/23 High St
Tel: 0116 251 6838

LIVERPOOL
52 Bold St
Tel: 0151 709 0866

LONDON

BUSINESS BOOK-SHOP, NW1
72 Park Road
Tel: 0171 723 3902

CAMDEN, NW1
128 Camden High St
Tel: 0171 284 4948

CHARING CROSS RD, WC2
121 Charing
Cross Rd
Tel: 0171 434 4291

CHEAPSIDE, EC2
145–147 Cheapside
Tel: 0171 726 6077

CHISWICK, W4
220-226 Chiswick
High Road
Tel: 0181 995 3559

THE CITY, EC3
1 Whittington Ave
Leadenhall Market
Tel: 0171 220 7882

CITY UNIVERSITY, EC1
Northampton
Square
Tel: 0171 608 0706

COVENT GARDEN, WC2
9 Garrick St
Tel: 0171 836 6757

EALING, W5
64 Ealing Broadway
Centre
Tel: 0181 840 5905

EARL'S COURT, SW5
266 Earl's Court Rd
Tel: 0171 370 1616

ECONOMIST BOOK-STORE, WC2
Clare Market
Portugal Street
Tel: 0171 405 5531

GOLDSMITHS', SE14
Goldsmiths' College,
New Cross
Tel: 0181 469 0262

HAMPSTEAD, NW3
68 Hampstead
High St
Tel: 0171 794 1098

HARRODS, SW1
87 Brompton Rd
Tel: 0171 730 1234

IMPERIAL COLLEGE, SW7
Imperial College Rd
Tel: 0171 589 3563

IMPERIAL COLLEGE SCHOOL OF MEDICINE
Charing Cross
Campus
Reynolds Building
St Dunstan's Rd
Tel: 0181 748 9768

Hammersmith
Campus
Commonwealth
Building
Du Cane Road
Tel: 0181 742 9600

ISLINGTON, N1
11 Islington Green
Tel: 0171 704 2280

KENSINGTON, W8
193 Kensington
High St
Tel: 0171 937 8432

KING'S COLLEGE, WC2
Macadam House
Surrey Street
Tel: 0171 836 0205

KING'S ROAD, SW3
150-152 King's Road
Tel: 0171 351 2023

LONDON GUILD-HALL UNIVERSITY, E1
Calcutta House
Old Castle Street
Tel: 0171 247 0727

NOTTING HILL, W11
39 Notting Hill Gate
Tel: 0171 229 9444

OLD BROMPTON RD, SW7
99 Old Brompton Rd
Tel: 0171 581 8522

QUEEN MARY & WESTFIELD, E1
329 Mile End Road
Tel: 0181 980 2554

THAMES VALLEY UNIVERSITY, W5
St. Mary's Road &
Westel House, Ealing
Tel: 0181 840 6205

TRAFALGAR SQUARE, WC2
The Grand Building
Tel: 0171 839 4411

WIMBLEDON, SW19
12 Wimbledon
Bridge
Tel: 0181 543 9899

LUTON
University of Luton
Park Square
Tel: 01582 402704

MAIDSTONE
19 Earl St
Tel: 01622 681112

MACCLESFIELD
47 Mill St
Tel: 01625 424212

MAILING SERVICE
Tel: 01225 448595
Fax: 01225 444732

MANCHESTER
91 Deansgate
Tel: 0161 832 1992

MANCHESTER AIRPORT
Terminal 1 Airside
Tel: 0161 489 3405

MERRY HILL
95/96 Merry Hill
Shopping Centre
Brierley Hill
Tel: 01384 751551

MIDDLESBROUGH
9 Newton Mall
Cleveland Centre
Tel: 01642 242682

University of
Teesside
Middlesbrough
Tel: 01642 242017

MILTON KEYNES
51-53 Silbury Arcade
Tel: 01908 696260

570 Silbury
Boulevard
Tel: 01908 607454

NEWBURY
64 Northbrook St
Tel: 01635 569998

NEWCASTLE
104 Grey St
Tel: 0191 261 6140

NORTHAMPTON
19 Abington St
Tel: 01604 634854

NORWICH
21–24 Royal Arcade
Tel: 01603 632426

University of
East Anglia
Tel: 01603 453625

NOTTINGHAM
1–5 Bridlesmith Gate
Tel: 0115 948 4499

OXFORD
William Baker
House
Broad Street
Tel: 01865 790212

PERTH
St John's Centre
Tel: 01738 630013

PETERBOROUGH
6 Queensgate
Tel: 01733 313476

PLYMOUTH
65/69 New
George St
Tel: 01752 256699

PRESTON
3–5 Fishergate
Tel: 01772 555766

READING
89a Broad St
Tel: 01189 581270

Reading University
Whiteknights
Tel: 01189 874858

RICHMOND-UPON-THAMES
2–6 Hill St
Tel: 0181 332 1600

SALISBURY
7/9 High St
Tel: 01722 415596

SCARBOROUGH
97-98 Westborough
Tel: 01723 500414

SHEFFIELD
24 Orchard Sq
Tel: 0114 272 8971

Meadowhall Centre
26 The Arcade
Tel: 0114 256 8495

SHREWSBURY
18–19 High St
Tel: 01743 248112

SOLIHULL
67-71 High Street
Tel: 0121 711 2454

SOUTHAMPTON
69 Above Bar
Tel: 01703 633130

Southampton
Medical School,
Southampton
General Hospital
Tel: 01703 780602

University of
Southampton
Highfield
Tel: 01703 558267

SOUTHEND-ON-SEA
49–55 High St
Tel: 01702 437480

SOUTHPORT
367 Lord St
Tel: 01704 501088

ST. ALBANS
8/10 Catherine
Street
Tel: 01727 868866

STIRLING
Thistle Marches
Tel: 01786 478756

STOCKPORT
103 Princes St
Tel: 0161 477 3755

STOKE
Staffordshire
University Bookshop
Station Road
Tel: 01782 746318

STRATFORD-UPON-AVON
18 The High St
Tel: 01789 414418

SUTTON
71-81 High St
Tel: 0181 770 0404

SWANSEA
17 Oxford St
Tel: 01792 463567

Taliesin Arts Centre
University of Wales
Singleton Park
Tel: 01792 281460

SWINDON
27 Regent St
Tel: 01793 488838

TAUNTON
County Hotel
East St
Tel: 01823 333113

TUNBRIDGE WELLS
32/40 Calverley Rd
Tel: 01892 535446

ULSTER
Central Buildings
University of Ulster
Cromore Rd
Coleraine
Tel: 01265 324 735

WATFORD
174–176 The
Harlequin Centre,
High St
Tel: 01923 218197

Wall Hall Campus
Aldenham
Tel: 01707 285745

WINCHESTER
The Brooks
Middle Brook Street
Tel: 01962 866206

WOLVERHAMPTON
13-15 Victoria Street
Tel: 01902 427219

University of
Wolverhampton
Wulfruna Street
Tel: 01902 322435

Dudley Campus
Castle View
Tel: 01902 323374

Shropshire Campus
Priors Lee
Telford
Tel: 01902 323815

WORCESTER
95 High St
Tel: 01905 723397

WREXHAM
9/11 Regent Street
Tel: 01978 357444

YORK
28–29 High
Ousegate
Tel: 01904 628740